CONTENTS

Practice makes perfect.

Applied English Essentials is a book in which you can practice as you learn. You read about the basic rules of correct grammar and sentence structure, and then you have an opportunity to put them into practice.

The book is divided into 23 units. Units 1–17 are four pages each, and Units 18–23 have been expanded to six pages.

Here is how the book is arranged:

INFORMATION. In the first 17 units, there are two pages of instruction that outline the rules of grammar. They are illustrated with plenty of examples. The last six units have four pages of instruction, containing more complex and extensive material.

PRACTICE. At the bottom of these INFORMATION pages is a variety of exercises reinforcing the rules just taught. You can check your answers at the back of the book.

APPLICATION. On the remaining two pages of each unit you apply what you have learned by answering 25 questions. These pages are perforated for easy removal. The 25 questions provide uniform scoring.

RECAP. After every three to four units is a two-page RECAP which reviews the rules of grammar you have learned. The most important guidelines from the preceding units are restated, and then you answer 20 questions based on these guidelines.

OVERVIEW. At the end of the book is a two-page overview in which material from all 23 units is reviewed in a 50-question exercise.

This book provides all the essentials necessary to a good understanding of standard English, both spoken and written. As you read and practice, you'll learn the modern usages of grammar that you'll need to know in business and everyday life.

UNIT 1
The Sentence

Subjects ▽ Predicates ▽ Agreement

The basic grouping of words into a complete thought is called a *sentence*. To express a complete thought, a sentence must have a subject and a predicate.

Susan reads.

In the example above, *Susan* is the subject and *reads* is the predicate.

Subjects. The *subject* is the part of the sentence about which something is said.

A subject that refers to a single person or thing is a *singular subject*. The subject of the next example refers to one person: *Tom*.

Tom listens.

The subject of each of the following examples also refers to one person.

Milton works.
Karen reads.

In the next example, however, the subject refers to more than one person. A subject that means two or more persons or things is a *plural subject*.

Students study.

Other sentences with plural subjects include:

Horses run.
Dogs bark.

The *simple subject* is the word or words that the predicate tells about. Words that expand or explain the meaning of the simple subject are called *modifiers*. The simple subject with all its modifiers is called the *complete subject*.

Tom, the good student, **listens.**
The good students **are listening.**

In the examples above, the complete subjects are in italics. The simple subjects are *Tom* and *students*, respectively. Notice that the complete subject can be either singular or plural.

PRACTICE. In each sentence below, put parentheses around the simple subject, underline the words that make up the complete subject, and write **S** or **P** in the blank at the right of each sentence to indicate whether the simple subject is singular or plural.

---

1. Many high performance microphones were sold. _____

2. The companies with reliable annual reports succeed. _____

3. The takeover of the small firm by the corporation is disappointing. _____

4. A typewritten set of specifications for the job is enclosed. _____

5. Graphic designs of good quality communicate. _____

6. The effective company president deliberates. _____

7. The mimes, drummers, and baton twirlers are marching. _____

8. Several differing opinions about the completion of the highway were voiced. _____

9. The habitual runner-up tries. _____

10. The camera shops in the shopping district were closed. _____

Predicates. The *predicate* of the sentence tells what the subject is or does. It can be a single word but that word is always a verb. It may show action, possession, existence, or occurrence. In the sentences below, the verb, which begins the predicate, is marked in italics.

The secretary of our Chicago office *wrote* to you yesterday.

The Fulton Company *has* a large stock of our plastic containers.

That et store *is* the largest distributor of boa nstrictors in this area.

The ld house *burned* rapidly.

A s gle verb that tells what the subject is or do is the *simple predicate.*

T e secretary wrote.

** e secretaries are writing.**

 the examples above, *wrote* and *are writing* re the simple predicates.

However, very few sentences contain just a simple predicate. Words are usually added to expand or modify the meaning of the simple predicate. The simple predicate with its modifiers is called the *complete predicate.*

The secretary wrote to you yesterday.

The complete predicate of the example above is *wrote to you yesterday.*

Agreement. If the subject is singular, the predicate must also be singular. If the subject is plural, the predicate must also be plural. This fact of grammar is called the *agreement* of the predicate with the subject.

The president of the firms was at the meeting.

Notice that the simple subject of the example above is *president*, which is singular. Therefore, the simple predicate, *was*, is also singular.

PRACTICE. In each sentence below, put parentheses around the simple subject and underline the complete predicate.

1. Each of our salespeople sends in a daily report.

2. Most of the credit for the successful promotion goes to Mr. Sawyer.

3. The exact meaning of these legal words and phrases is given on page 289.

4. Large amounts of clothing are donated to the organization every month.

5. Elite Computer's wonderful word processing systems are on display around the world.

6. The fast-food restaurant served delicious fried chicken.

7. The magazine's subscriptions increased last year.

8. The ventures of the investment firm were under scrutiny.

9. Systems for solar heating were incorporated into the architect's design.

10. The telephone wires were replaced by flexible plastic tubing that transmitted sound.

11. Last year's sharp price increases caused a jump in the earnings chart.

12. He advocated curbing profits to inject new vigor into the market.

UNIT 1 ▽ APPLICATION

The Sentence

In each sentence below, the predicate forms are in parentheses. One is singular; the other is plural. Write the correct form in the blank at the right. (It may help you to circle the simple subject before deciding.)

For Scoring

1. That statement (doesn't, don't) sound right to me.   _____ ____

2. An extra charge for the ten barrels of apples (is, are) indicated on the invoice.   _____ ____

3. One of the radios (transmits, transmit) a signal over a 1,000-mile radius.   _____ ____

4. An itemized statement (was, were) mailed to you on the first of the month.   _____ ____

5. This new job (surpasses, surpass) my expectations.   _____ ____

6. Only one of these proofs (goes, go) back to the printer.   _____ ____

7. A single carload of potatoes (feeds, feed) the men for a week.   _____ ____

8. The number of overdue accounts (is, are) still growing.   _____ ____

9. Each one of the bundles (contains, contain) a designated number of sponges.   _____ ____

10. The Weber Process Company (is, are) doing our work now.   _____ ____

11. A food processor with the two attachments (costs, cost) $225.   _____ ____

12. The construction of the bridges (completes, complete) the work for this year.   _____ ____

13. The installations (meets, meet) our present needs.   _____ ____

14. Each employee (adds, add) up her own expenses for the month.   _____ ____

15. Life insurers (decides, decide) whether or not to lend

    money to their clients. _____ ____

16. Opportunities for land acquisition (looks, look) dismal for

    the future. _____ ____

17. He is one of the managers who (agrees, agree) that lower

    rates will prevent losses. _____ ____

18. One of the paper carriers (walks, walk) instead of riding

    his bike. _____ ____

19. A new set of economic statistics (is, are) needed for

    bankers. _____ ____

20. The dry process photocopiers (pays, pay) for the

    expensive paper in the long run. _____ ____

> In each group of sentences below, only one choice sh.. 's the correct agreement of the predicate with the subject. Wr\. the letter of the correct choice in the blank at the right.

21. a. The general interest in the status of both firms were significant.
    b. The assets of the estate is phenomenal.
    c. The quality of the stocks they bought is deteriorating.
    d. The success of many investors are considered easy to explain. ____ ____

22. a. Collecting coins are no longer just a hobby, but an investment.
    b. A collection of just 50 commemorative silver half-dollars is now worth many thousands of dollars.
    c. Rolls of money is sorted through to find a cherished coin.
    d. Specialization of coin collectors are now a key to possible wealth. ____ ____

23. a. Earnings' growth are faster when market averages keep up with inflation.
    b. Investment strategies is crucial in times of recession.
    c. The best choice of the analysts are the big utilities.
    d. Companies sensitive to interest rates are growing rapidly. ____ ____

24. a. Students are eligible to borrow money for college.
    b. Guaranteed student loans is subsidized by the government.
    c. Students attending a trade school at least half of the time is eligible for the federal loans.
    d. Knowing the programs are the key to finding a loan. ____ ____

25. a. Federal pension law, women's rights groups, and pension reform organizations disagrees over pension benefits.
    b. Congress and the pension industry are arguing over the fairness of an ex-wife's claims to her husband's assets.
    c. Individual Retirement Accounts is recommended as one solution.
    d. Compromise solutions is suggested by some legal scholars. ____ ____

UNIT 2
Nouns and Their Plurals

Common and proper nouns ▽
Plurals of nouns

Common and proper nouns. A *noun* is a word that is used as a name. A *common noun* names one in a general group of persons, places, or things. A *proper noun*, on the other hand, is the name applied to a particular one of a group.

Notice the difference between common and proper nouns below. The common noun is the *general* name; the proper noun is the *specific* name. All proper nouns must begin with a capital letter.

Each noun at the top of the next column names only one person, place, or thing. Therefore, each is a *singular* noun.

Common noun	Proper noun
woman	Abigail Adams
river	Mississippi
language	English
state	Maine
country	Ireland

Plurals of nouns. The *plural* form of the noun names more than one person, place, or thing. For most nouns, simply add *s* to form the plural.

American	continent	language
Americans	continents	languages
book	pen	chair
books	pens	chairs

However, some plurals require other additions. The final letter of a noun determines the way its plural is formed. For nouns ending in *s*, *ss*, *z*, *x*, *sh*, or *ch*, add *es*.

circus	glass	topaz
circuses	glasses	topazes
tax	lash	church
taxes	lashes	churches

PRACTICE. In each sentence below, a noun in singular form is shown in parentheses. Write its plural form in the blank at the right and capitalize proper nouns.

1. Did the employees get their end-of-the-year (bonus) yet? _____

2. Please see if there are any wooden kitchen (match) in the cabinet. _____

3. The (spaniard) colonized much of the New World. _____

4. Do (sphinx) always have the body of a lion and the head of a man? _____

5. They ordered three large (pizza). _____

6. The hikers found several different kinds of (tree) in the forest. _____

7. The pilot saw an antelope running through the (badland) of South

   Dakota. _____

8. The (bus) all displayed public service advertisements. _____

9. Five plane (crash) were reported that day. _____

10. How many (waltz) has the orchestra played? _____

11. The (stress) of daily life affect us all. _____

To form the plurals of nouns ending in *y* preceded by a vowel, add *s*. (The vowels are *a*, *e*, *i*, *o*, and *u*. When *y* is pronounced like *i*, it functions as a vowel. All the other letters in the alphabet are consonants.)

alley	journey	attorney
alleys	**journeys**	**attorneys**

To form the plurals of nouns ending in *y* preceded by a consonant, change the *y* to *i* and add *es*.

lily	company	facility
lilies	**companies**	**facilities**

To form the plurals of nouns ending in *o* preceded by a vowel, add *s*.

folio	studio	ratio
folios	**studios**	**ratios**

When a noun ends in *o* preceded by a consonant, add *es*.

calico	cargo	tomato
calicoes	**cargoes**	**tomatoes**

However, there are exceptions to this principle, such as the words listed below. Consult your dictionary to determine the correct spelling of words about which you are not sure.

bingo	ditto	piano
bingos	**dittos**	**pianos**

Form the plurals of most nouns ending in *f* by adding *s*.

roof	chief	sheriff
roofs	**chiefs**	**sheriffs**

belief	waif	plaintiff
beliefs	**waifs**	**plaintiffs**

However, the plurals of many nouns ending in *f* or *fe* require the changing of the *f* or *fe* to a *v* before adding *es*.

half	knife	wife
halves	**knives**	**wives**

The plural of some nouns may be formed in more than one way.

volcano	hoof
volcanoes	**hooves**
volcanos	**hoofs**

cargo	bus
cargoes	**buses**
cargos	**busses**

PRACTICE. In each sentence below, a noun in singular form is shown in parentheses. Write its plural form in the blank at the right.

1. The (country) reached an agreement that was to their
   mutual advantage.   _____

2. Do (wolf) always travel in packs?   _____

3. A system of (pulley) facilitated the construction work.   _____

4. Employment (agency) have records about jobs all over the
   country.   _____

5. The (thief) found a set of important papers in the wall safe. _____

6. Let's hear more volume from the (soprano)!   _____

7. The eagle soared over the (cliff).   _____

8. The old house had three (chimney).   _____

9. How many (loaf) of bread will fit in the oven?   _____

UNIT 2 ▽ APPLICATION

Nouns and Their Plurals

In each sentence below, a noun in singular form is shown in parentheses. Write its plural form in the blank at the right of each sentence.

For
Scoring

1. Fog settled into the many (valley) bordering the highway. _____ ____

2. The (echo) reminded him of boomerangs. _____ ____

3. The eastern autumn owes its color to the (leaf) of

   deciduous trees. _____ ____

4. Who are your favorite baseball (hero)? _____ ____

5. Pewter and bronze are (alloy). _____ ____

6. The ice skater wore (earmuff). _____ ____

7. Human (society) usually have some kind of hierarchy. _____ ____

8. Why is it said that cats have nine (life)? _____ ____

9. The circuitry problem caused the computer to print nothing

   but (zero). _____ ____

10. There are no (vacancy) at this time. _____ ____

11. The river was dotted with (skiff). _____ ____

12. The professor had studied (volcano) all his life, but had

    never seen one erupt. _____ ____

13. Modern (library) make use of computer catalogs and

    checkout systems. _____ ____

14. William Frederick Cody was contracted to kill a certain

    number of (buffalo) each day to feed the cavalry. _____ ____

15. The (veto) were expected to cause only a temporary delay

    in the passage of the legislation. _____ ____

16. Many (safe) depend on combination locks for their

    security. _____ ____

17. Coral (reef) have been known to stop huge ships. ＿＿＿＿＿＿ ＿＿＿

18. What are the (ratio) of men to women and college

   graduates to high school graduates in today's job market? ＿＿＿＿＿＿ ＿＿＿

19. The (shelf) were designed to store computer printouts. ＿＿＿＿＿＿ ＿＿＿

20. Are you familiar with any folk (remedy) based on popular

   knowledge and beliefs about certain herbs? ＿＿＿＿＿＿ ＿＿＿

> For each item below, choose the sentence that contains the correct plural form of the italicized noun. Write the letter matching the sentence in the blank at the right.

21. a. The *attornies* argued their case.
    b. The *torpedos* rocketed toward their targets
    c. Airport workers unload the *cargoes*.
    d. All of the *tomatos* were destroyed by some kind of insect. ＿＿＿ ＿＿＿

22. a. *Sheafs* are the stalks and ears of a cereal grass, bound together.
    b. In the cartoon, a group of *dwarfs* inhabit the forest.
    c. Even when under pressure, the prisoner would not compromise his *believes*.
    d. The box contained several lace *handkerchiefs* ＿＿＿ ＿＿＿

23. a. The visitors' *sympathys* were directed towards one small boy.
    b. He smiled and attempted shyly to return their courtesis.
    c. Although the director was not fond of *charityses*, he permitted the donation of some new clothing and toys.
    d. The orphan was not accustomed to such *luxuries*. ＿＿＿ ＿＿＿

24. a. The supermarket manager worried that the shipment of *turkeyes* would not arrive before Thanksgiving.
    b. He sent *envoies* to the various farms and packing firms
    c. Had the *trolleys* been running on a regular schedule, the messengers may have had better luck solving the problems.
    d. As it turned out, everything seemed to go wrong; even the *pulleze* in the conveyor system gave way at the packing firm. ＿＿＿ ＿＿＿

25. a. The registrants were told what *duties* would be expected of them.
    b. "Failure to comply with these rules," the commander said, "would result in severe *penaltyse*."
    c. The nation's *boundarys* and honor were dependent on their success.
    d. The successful completion of the task at hand would result in unlimited *glorys* for all involved. ＿＿＿ ＿＿＿

UNIT 3
Plurals of Irregular and Foreign Nouns

Irregular nouns ▽
Letters and figures ▽
Foreign nouns

Irregular nouns. The plurals of some nouns are formed irregularly. There is no rule for their formation; they must be learned through study and usage. The best policy is to check any unfamiliar words in a dictionary.

child	foot	woman	goose
children	feet	women	geese

mouse	ox	man	tooth
mice	oxen	men	teeth

A few nouns have the same form for both the singular and the plural. They do not require the addition of an *s* to form the plural.

Chinese	trout	deer	series
mackerel	sheep	salmon	species

A few other nouns look like plurals but are sometimes singular in meaning. They may require a singular predicate when used in a sentence.

civics	economics	mathematics
news	physics	politics

These words are singular when they refer to areas of study or an otherwise all-encompassing subject.

Notice the agreement of subject and predicate in this sentence.

The bad *news is* that there was a fire; the good *news is* that we'll have to relocate the offices.

Notice how the words in these sentences are used in their plural form.

The *economics* of the situation *were* difficult to understand.

Their *politics were* varied.

On the other hand, there are some nouns that are always plural in meaning as well as in appearance. They have no singular forms.

cattle	clothes	proceeds

PRACTICE. In each sentence below, the singular form of a noun is given in parentheses. Write the plural form in the blank at the right.

1. The treasurer presented several (series) of figures. _____

2. Most of the (postman) used jeeps. _____

3. All (proceeds) will be donated to the building fund. _____

4. The (goose) left in a flurry of loudly flapping wings. _____

5. The (sheep) seemed almost unending as they crossed the

   road. _____

6. The (saleswoman) were familiar with all the merchandise. _____

7. Benjamin did not want to have his (tooth) straightened. _____

8. What is your degree of expertise in (mathematics)? _____

9. Amphibian (species) inhabit the swamp. _____

10. Are there any publishers of books for (child) here in town? _____

Letters and figures. Form the plural of a letter that appears alone or with other single letters by adding *s* only. When simply adding *s* would cause confusion, add an apostrophe and then an *s*. Add *'s* to all lowercase letters and to some capital letters.

The child knows his ABCs.
Cross your t's and dot your i's.
I got all A's.

Do not use an apostrophe to form the plural of a figure that appears alone.

Number 8s are on the shelf.

Foreign nouns. Some nouns came from other languages and are used in English in their original form. The original plural forms are also used for most of these nouns, although in the course of time, usage has developed English plurals for some of them.

To form the plural of a noun ending in *is*, change the *is* to *es*.

analysis	basis
analyses	bases

To form the plural of a noun ending in *on*, change the *on* to *a*.

criterion	phenomenon
criteria	phenomena

Notice that *phenomenon* could also be made plural by adding an *s* to form *phenomenons*.

To form the plural of a noun ending in *um*, change the *um* to *a*.

medium	datum
media	data

Notice that the plurals of many of these foreign words have also adopted the English pattern of adding an *s. Gymnasium* may, for example, be *gymnasiums* or *gymnasia*.

To form the plural of a foreign noun ending in *us*, change the *us* to an *i*.

alumnus	stimulus	nucleus
alumni	stimuli	nuclei

To form the plural of a noun ending in *a*, change *a* to *ae*.

alumna	vertebra
alumnae	vertebrae

However, the plural of some foreign nouns may be formed by adding *s* or *e. Formula* becomes *formulas* or *formulae*.

Compound nouns. Compound nouns written as solid words form the plural in the same way as other nouns. Compound nouns written with hyphens make the first, or principal, noun plural.

bookkeeper	son-in-law
bookkeepers	sons-in-law

PRACTICE. In each sentence below, the singular form of a noun is given in parentheses. Write the plural form in the blank at the right.

1. The students expressed an interest in ESP, UFOs, and other unexplained (phenomenon). _____

2. The (nucleus) of the cells will absorb the violet dye. _____

3. What are the (curriculum) at the business college? _____

4. The (criterion) for the job included a high school diploma. _____

5. Members of the public relations department hope that the (prospectus) will confirm the need for an employee magazine and a newsletter. _____

6. All mammals have (vertebra). _____

7. The news (medium) reported the events. _____

UNIT 3 ▽ APPLICATION

Plurals of Irregular and Foreign Nouns

Write the plural form of each noun in parentheses in the space at the right.

For
Scoring

1. (Crisis) of one kind or another strike every business.   _____ ____

2. The (datum) about the circulation of these magazines are given on the enclosed sheets.   _____ ____

3. Many (alumnus) of the school occupy prominent positions in the business community.   _____ ____

4. (Analysis) of all our products have been made by the Food and Drug Administration.   _____ ____

5. Credit (memorandum) for the shipments you returned are enclosed.   _____ ____

6. (Parenthesis) are sometimes used to enclose figures that further explain a numeric amount.   _____ ____

7. The (basis) of the report were Mr. Maxwell's remarks at a recent meeting.   _____ ____

8. (Bacterium) sometimes destroy harmful germs.   _____ ____

9. Silk (clothes) are often more decorative than functional.   _____ ____

10. The young (woman) formed a firm that used all of their names in its title.   _____ ____

11. Increased production and other (stimulus) should help the economy.   _____ ____

12. The (German) and the Turks were allies during the First World War.   _____ ____

13. Rainbows are (phenomenon) of physical science. _____ ____

14. The (formula) are not available to the general public. _____ ____

15. Do you understand Marshall McLuhan's concept of the

 mass (medium)? _____ ____

16. The college campus had two (gymnasium). _____ ____

17. Lemuel Gulliver and Bob Cratchit were both (Englishman). _____ ____

18. Animals that have backbones are said to have (vertebra). _____ ____

19. How many (axis) does the Earth have? _____ ____

20. Each department chairman was asked to submit several

 possible (curriculum) for the next semester. _____ ____

In each item below, choose the sentence that contains the correct
form of the plural nouns. Write the letter of that sentence in the
blank at the right.

21. a. There was a large herd of oxes.
 b. Mr. Van der Bleks is six feets tall.
 c. The men, women, and childs were all saved from disaster.
 d. They theorized that eating in the office caused the arrival of
 several mice. _____ ____

22. a. He went into the woods to hunt deers.
 b. The boy fished all day and caught many mackerel.
 c. No circle has two radiis.
 d. Salmons swim upstream to spawn. _____ ____

23. a. Civics is a subject once taught in all junior high schools.
 b. Economics are a hard subject to teach.
 c. Mathematics are not popular with many students.
 d. The United States are one of the greatest countries in the world. _____ ____

24. a. The herd of cattles was small.
 b. The premiseses of the bank is well guarded.
 c. The proceed of the sales promotion is already spent on
 advertising.
 d. The sales manager's statistics are always accurate. _____ ____

25. a. The secretary always mistyped the xs.
 b. All the 9's in the column were incorrect.
 c. She never remembered to dot her i's.
 d. His 8s always looked like 3's. _____ ____

UNITS 1–3 ▽ RECAP

The Sentence ▽ Nouns and Their Plurals ▽ Plurals of Irregular and Foreign Nouns

Here are the highlights of the guides relating to the sentence and its subject and predicate, nouns and their plurals, and the plurals of irregular and foreign nouns.

The sentence. To express a complete thought, a sentence must have a subject and a predicate.

Number in subjects and predicates. Subjects and predicates can be either singular or plural.

Complete subjects or predicates. The simple subject with all its modifiers is called the complete subject; the simple predicate with all its modifiers is called the complete predicate.

Agreement. The subject determines whether the predicate should be singular or plural.

Common and proper nouns. A common noun refers to one in a general group of persons, places, things, or ideas; a proper noun applies to a particular one of a group.

Plurals of nouns. In general, nouns form their plurals by adding *s* or *es.*

Irregular nouns. The plurals of some nouns do not depend on rules for their formation. These irregular plurals must be learned.

Nouns with only one form. Some nouns are always plural.

Foreign nouns. Some foreign nouns form their plurals according to the English pattern; others form their plurals based on their foreign endings.

Read the example sentences below to determine which correctly illustrates the guide indicated. Write the letter of the best sentence in the blank at the right.

For
Scoring

1. Common noun.
   a) Mary sang.
   b) Many students sang.   _____   _____

2. Number in subjects and predicates—plural.
   a) Both Jane and Alice can dance and sing.
   b) Cynthia only likes to dance.   _____   _____

3. Plurals of nouns.
   a) The club contributed to all three churches.
   b) The church received a generous gift. _____ _____

4. Agreement of subject and predicate.
   a) All the girls in the group were late.
   b) The girls in the group was late. _____ _____

5. Plurals of foreign nouns.
   a) All the curriculum were approved for next year.
   b) All the curricula were approved for next year. _____ _____

6. Use of apostrophe in numbers and letters.
   a) All the size 7's were sold by noon.
   b) He didn't even remember to dot his i's. _____ _____

7. Sentence—complete thought.
   a) Thinking of his family, he returned home.
   b) Thinking of what a sad time it was. _____ _____

8. Nouns with only one form.
   a) The boy and his father caught six salmons.
   b) There were three fresh mackerel left for sale. _____ _____

9. Irregular nouns—plural.
   a) There were several mouses in the school.
   b) The hunters shot many deer. _____ _____

10. Irregular nouns—singular.
    a) The economics of the situation dictate that we save rather than spend.
    b) He says that mathematics is not his best subject. _____ _____

In the following sentences, underline the correct form of the words in parentheses.

11. Her question about the retirement plans (has, have) been received. _____

12. A complete supply of paper and envelopes (was, were) shipped today. _____

13. The first attorney accused the other two (attorneys, attornies) of fraud. _____

14. The farrier made new shoes for the horses' (hooves, hoofs). _____

15. Many (churchs, churches) profit from tax exemption. _____

16. The foreign (woman, women) were all afraid to be interviewed. _____

17. All the (alumna, alumnae) of the college were sent the bulletin. _____

18. She enjoyed studying (english, English). _____

19. There were several (criterions, criteria) on which she based her decision. _____

20. There are no more size (8's, 8s) available. _____

UNIT 4
Pronouns and Their Antecedents

Possessive pronouns ▽
Second person pronouns

Pronouns. A *pronoun* is a word used in place of a noun. Instead of using his own name, for example, a speaker says *I*. Familiar forms of the personal pronouns are:

	Singular	Plural
First person (the speaker)	I	we
Second person (the one spoken to)	you	you
Third person (the one spoken about)	he, she, it	they

The third person singular pronoun has three forms: *he* refers to a man, *she* to a woman, and *it* to an object. We speak of these pronouns as having *masculine*, *feminine*, or *neuter* gender, respectively.

Possessive pronouns. Each personal pronoun has its own possessive form, which is not spelled with apostrophes.

PERSONAL PRONOUNS		POSSESSIVE FORMS	
I	me	my	mine
we	us	our	ours
you	you	your	yours
he	him	his	his
she	her	her	hers
who	whom	whose	whose
it	it	its	its
they	them	their	theirs

Antecedents. The word the pronoun takes the place of is called the *antecedent* of that pronoun. In the following example, the antecedent is *salesman* and the pronoun is *he*.

The *salesman* thought *he* could sell the company's goods and services.

In the next example, the antecedent is *records* and the pronoun is *they*.

The *records* of the company were checked, and *they* were found to be accurate.

PRACTICE. In the following sentences, underline the antecedent; underline the pronoun *twice*; and write **P** over the antecedent if it is plural and **S** if it is singular.

1. Our products are made of natural ingredients, and they are sure to please.

2. If the papers arrive, they will be held here.

3. The proofs were ready yesterday, but they cannot be mailed until tomorrow.

4. A stenographer cannot hope to get anywhere unless she knows English grammar.

5. The members have agreed that we should go ahead with the plans.

6. Did Henry say why he called?

7. Sharon, will you be able to explain the procedures to the new employee?

8. The typewriter was discarded because it was irreparable.

9. The president has promised that she will address the members of the board.

A pronoun must agree with its antecedent in person, number, and gender. There are three persons—first, second, and third. There are two numbers—singular and plural. There are three genders—masculine, feminine, and neuter.

If the antecedent is *plural*, the pronoun referring to it must be *plural*; if the antecedent is in the *third* person, the pronoun referring to it must be in the *third* person; if the antecedent is *feminine*, the pronoun referring to it must be feminine. This act of grammar is called the *agreement* of the pronoun with its antecedent.

When the gender of a singular antecedent is not known, it has been common practice to use the *masculine* pronoun in referring to that antecedent.

Every student was given a different assignment, and *he* is held responsible for that assignment.

It is also appropriate to use the feminine pronoun in such cases, or to use both masculine and feminine.

Every student was given a different as- signment, and *she* is held responsible for that assignment.

Nevertheless, a plural pronoun is never used to refer to a singular antecedent. Notice how the singular pronouns *he* and *she* agree with the singular antecedent *person* in this sentence:

A *person* can't go on a long trip unless *he or she* makes plans in advance.

Second person pronouns. Whether singular or plural, second person pronouns are always followed by the plural predicate form. Notice the use of the word *you* in the sentences below. Even though *you* represents only one person, the plural predicate forms are used.

You *are* a good student.
You *were* a good student.
You *have been* a good student.

Contrast this treatment of the second person pronoun *you* with the third person pronoun *she*, which also represents only one person:

She *is* a good student.
She *was* a good student.
She *has been* a good student.

PRACTICE. Underline the antecedent in each sentence and fill in the correct pronoun.

1. Miss Smith said that _____ would return in an hour.

2. The operator carefully explained what _____ had done.

3. Let Mr. Howard sharpen the scissors so that _____ will cut better.

4. The members of the committee all agreed that _____ should supply the funds.

5. Everyone did just what _____ was told to do.

6. The cattle were put up for sale, and _____ brought a good price.
   Write the correct predicate form in the blank.

7. You _____ still reading that book when I saw you three weeks ago. (were, was)

8. I believe you _____ made a mistake in the estimate. (have, has)

9. You _____ the very person for whom I have been looking. (is, are)

UNIT 4 ▽ APPLICATION

Pronouns and Their Antecedents

In each of these sentences, underline the antecedent *once* and the pronoun *twice*. Write **P** over the antecedent if it is plural and **S** if it is singular.

For Scoring

1. That movie theater has been in the city for many years, and it is now badly in need of renovation.   _____

2. Premium discounts are an enticement to shoppers, and they are evidently effective.   _____

3. The jury deliberated for three days until they agreed on the verdict.   _____

4. There are differences of pronunciation between New England and the South, and they sometimes cause confusion.   _____

5. Kathy and Raymond got the most votes, and they will be class president and vice-president.   _____

6. The reader has difficulty following the argument when it is not logical.   _____

7. He will work on the job until it is finished.   _____

8. Everyone should be aware of her own best assets.   _____

9. When the crowd had assembled, the speaker addressed them.   _____

10. A person is known by the company she keeps.   _____

In the following sentences, select the letter of the correct sentence.

11. a. Each student has the habit of putting off *his* study until the night before the test.
    b. Each student has the habit of putting off *their* study until the night before the test.   _____ _____

12. a. Either of them are sure to be a good officer and do *their* work.
    b. Either of them is sure to be a good officer and do *her* work.   _____ _____

13. a. Anyone takes chances when *he* flies.
    b. Anyone takes chances when *they* fly.   _____ _____

14. a. The strongest man who *has* entered the contest said that he lost.
    b. The strongest man who *have* entered the contest said that he lost.   _____ _____

15. a. Jane and Mary *have* finished *their* assignments.
    b. Jane and Mary *has* finished *her* assignments. _____ _____

16. a. Neither Jane nor Mary *has* finished *her* test.
    b. Neither Jane nor Mary *have* finished *their* test. _____ _____

17. a. Everybody has *their* own solution to the world's problems.
    b. Everybody has *his* own solution to the world's problems. _____ _____

18. a. Each one asked permission to do *his* own thing.
    b. Each one asked permission to do *their* own thing. _____ _____

19. a. If either *Mike* or *Steve* applied, *he* would be selected for the job.
    b. If either *Mike* or *Steve* applied, *they* would be selected for the job. _____ _____

20. a. Everyone is doing *his* job.
    b. Everyone is doing *their* job. _____ _____

Write the letter of the *incorrect* sentence in the blank.

21. a. Each of the children was getting a new bike.
    b. The jury still disagreed after they argued all night.
    c. The policeman said he was selling tickets for the orphans' ball game.
    d. All the teachers were upset when you was late with the paychecks. _____ _____

22. a. The boy's club made enough money with their yard sale to buy new camping equipment.
    b. Each man makes a living in his own way.
    c. The players in the symphony all said they practice on their instruments every day.
    d. After the girls bought the new hats, they regretted their selections. _____ _____

23. a. Senior boys have been advised to choose the field of engineering for their future jobs.
    b. A philosophy professor argued that all the people in the world is off its rocker.
    c. A person should not eat before he goes to bed.
    d. Each member of the group gave just what he could. _____ _____

24. a. Some careless campers had failed to put out their fire.
    b. The suspects were forced to leave their fingerprints on file at the police station.
    c. Before a student is admitted to the college, you must pass an entrance exam.
    d. When the "common gender" is used, the masculine pronoun often replaces its antecedent. _____ _____

25. a. Pronouns agree with its antecedent in number, person, and gender.
    b. The word for which the pronoun is used is called its antecedent.
    c. The pronouns "you" and "it" can be used as either subject or object without changing their form.
    d. Alice and she saw the accident on their way home from school. _____ _____

UNIT 5
Verbs

Transitive ▽ Intransitive ▽ Linking ▽ Helping ▽ Tenses of verbs

Verbs. The subject of a sentence, as we have seen, is a noun or a pronoun. The predicate of a sentence is a *verb*, a word that shows action, existence, state of being, or possession. A complete thought cannot be conveyed without using a verb. In many ways the verb is the most important word in the sentence. Many errors in grammar occur because of incorrect verb usage.

Verbs are divided into four groups: transitive, intransitive, linking or conditioning, and helping.

Transitive. A transitive verb carries or transmits action from a subject to an object. The object *completes* the meaning of the verb. Transitive verbs *always* require an *object*.

He swung *the bat*.

The action denoted by the transitive verb takes effect on the object. He swung what? The bat.

Sometimes, an indirect object comes before the direct object.

He pitched me the ball.

Intransitive. An intransitive verb is a verb that does not require an object to complete the meaning.

They dance.

Some verbs can be either transitive or intransitive.

She plays. (intransitive)

She plays games. (transitive)

Linking. A linking verb is a verb that connects or links the subject of the sentence with the word that follows the simple predicate. The linking verb is a special kind of intransitive verb.

It is sometimes called a *condition verb* because it expresses a condition about the subject. All forms of the verb *to be* are linking verbs that set up a kind of equation between the subject and the word that comes after the verb.

Sarah *is* smart.

The baby *is* sick.

Other linking verbs are the sense words: *feel*, *smell*, *sound*, *taste*, and *look* (which can also be used transitively). The words *become*, *seem*, and *appear* are also commonly used linking verbs.

She felt the fabric. (transitive)

The fabric felt rough. (linking)

Helping. Forms of the verb *to be* are called *helping* (or *auxiliary*) verbs when used in combination with the main verb.

He *had* lost the key to his car.

The helping verb is needed in the formation of some tenses.

PRACTICE. Identify the italicized verbs in the following sentences as **T** for transitive, **I** for intransitive, and **L** for linking. Write the letter in the blank at the right.

---

1. She *looked* at the art objects in the downtown museum. _____

2. He *looked* sleepy all day long. _____

3. The ballet troupe from the Netherlands *danced*. _____

4. Gabrielle Henderson *fixed* her washing machine. _____

5. Bret Taggart has *pitched* four winning games. _____

6. The critic carefully *examined* the text of the poem. _____

Tenses of verbs. Tense is a word used to refer to the *time* shown by the verb. There are three primary tenses:

Present tense is used when we speak of the time that now is. **I work.**

Past tense refers to a time *before* the present. **I worked.**

Future tense refers to a time still to come. **I shall work.**

The third person singular of a verb differs slightly from the form used for the first and second person singular and plural and the third person plural.

Most verbs add *s* to form the third person singular. **Walk. She walks.**

Verbs ending in *y* preceded by a consonant change *y* to *i* and add *es* to form the third person singular. **Fly. He flies.**

Verbs ending in *o* preceded by a consonant add *es* in the third person singular. **Go. She goes.**

Verbs ending in *s, x, sh, ss,* and *ch* add *es* in the third person singular. **Pass. She passes.**

Verbs and Their Past Tense. The regular way to form the past tense of a verb is to add *ed.* Verbs that form their past tense in that way are therefore called *regular* verbs.

I accept. I accepted.
We enter. We entered.

If the verb already ends in *e*, add *d* only to form the past tense.

I believe. I believed.
I prove. He proved.

There are some special points in forming the past tense of regular verbs. A verb that ends with *y* preceded by a consonant changes *y* to *i* and adds *ed* to form the past tense.

We apply. We applied.
They study. They studied.

A verb of one syllable that ends with a single consonant preceded by a single vowel doubles the final consonant before adding *ed.*

They stop. They stopped.
We ship. We shipped.

A verb of two syllables that ends with a consonant immediately preceded by a single vowel and *that is accented on the last syllable* also doubles the final consonant before adding *ed.*

It occurs. It occurred.
He refers. He referred.
They transfer. They transferred.
I prefer. I preferred.

The double consonant only occurs when adding *ed* to form the past tense.

Progressive Tenses. In the present and past tenses, we can use the progressive tense to express continuous action. The progressive tenses are constructed with forms of the verb *to be* plus the *ing* form of main verb.

I am sitting. (present progressive)
I was sitting. (past progressive)

PRACTICE. In each of these blanks, write the three tenses of the verb form at left.
MODEL: He *studies.* He *is studying.* He *studied.* He *was studying.*

	Present Progressive	Past	Past Progressive
1. We comply.	_____	_____	_____
2. You disappoint.	_____	_____	_____
3. He assists.	_____	_____	_____
4. I commit.	_____	_____	_____
5. I plan.	_____	_____	_____

UNIT 5 ▽ APPLICATION

Verbs

Fill in the blank to the right of each of these sentences using the *present tense* of the verb printed in parentheses.

For
Scoring

1. One of the major department stores never (invest) its money efficiently. _____ ____

2. A large share of the company's profits (go) to the employees. _____ ____

3. Frequent sales (bring) more customers. _____ ____

4. The large number of employees leaving (cause) serious problems in the office. _____ ____

5. The supervisor (predict) better working hours. _____ ____

6. Mark (come) to the company with good references. _____ ____

7. That blouse (go) with your new skirt. _____ ____

8. Jeff (possess) the ability to get the job done. _____ ____

9. Your poor attitude (threaten) your job. _____ ____

10. Barbara (predict) she will enjoy her vacation. _____ ____

In each of these sentences, choose the *past tense* of the word in parentheses and write it in the blank at the right.

11. His report (embody) the main points of our discussion. _____ ____

12. The trouble was (remedy) without much delay. _____ ____

13. The error (occur) because he was not listening. _____ ____

14. She (report) that she had studied the letter carefully and had referred it to the home office. _____ ____

15. After it was discovered that the last paragraph had been (omit) from the report, the chief clerk conferred at once with the president. _____ ____

Identify the italicized verbs in the following sentences as **T** for transitive, **I** for intransitive, **L** for linking, and **H** for helping. Write the letter in the blank at the right.

16. The material in her new skirt *felt* like silk. _____ ____

17. He *smelled* the fresh baked pie when he opened the door. _____ _____

18. The athletic director has always *walked* in the evening. _____ _____

> In the following sentences, write the correct form of the personal pronoun in the blank.

19. She asked (he, him) to go to the prom. _____ _____

20. Angel mother presented (she, her) with a new car. _____ _____

> In each group of sentences below, there is one sentence in which the verb is used and spelled correctly. Write the letter of that sentence in the blank at the right.

21. a. e was compeled to come to trial for the offense.
    b. he judge concured with the opinion of the jury.
    The defense lawyer thought his client would be acquitted.
    According to the client, he had commited the offense to defend himself. _____ _____

22. a. The summer solstice occurrs every year in June.
    b. Because of long tradition, many countries celebrates this solstice with outdoor feasts and dancing.
    c. In Eastern Europe everyone go to large bonfires lit at night to mark this occasion.
    d. Sometimes old tribal rituals are embodied in the summer celebrations. _____ _____

23. a. The science that deals with the earth, the elements, and life is referred to as geography.
    b. Because of the study of geography, man is better equiped to deal with his environment.
    c. An understanding of climate, weather, and space relationships occurr in this study.
    d. Sometimes biology, chemistry, mathematics, and physics relates to the study of geography. _____ _____

24. a. He always omitts some items that he is supposed to include.
    b. He has work all week to improve his memory by reciting the list to himself many times.
    c. Lately, his remembrance of all the items occurs more frequently.
    d. It has been demonstrated that memory improve with practice. _____ _____

25. a. Ancient Egyptians are said to have maked the first leavened bread.
    b. Home-baked bread only qualify for the baking contest.
    c. Various kinds of bread comes in many shapes, sizes, and colors.
    d. Bread contributes to the basic daily nutrition of people around the world. _____ _____

UNIT 6
Verbs and Their Tenses

Future tense ▽
Secondary tenses ▽
Perfect tense confusion ▽
Emphatic tense forms

Future tense. The future tense is used to denote an action or a condition still to come. Verbs form their future tense with the helping verbs *will* and *shall*. Careful writers make a distinction in the use of these helping verbs.

When the subject is in the first person pronoun, use *shall* to form the future tense of the verb. This is the *simple* future tense; it refers to an action still to come.

We shall be pleased.

When the subject is in the second or third person, use *will* to form the future tense of the verb.

He will succeed.
It will occur.
You will graduate.

Sometimes, however, you want to express *strong determination* when you use the future tense. In that case, you reverse the use of *shall* and *will*. Use *will* with the first person to express strong determination, and use *shall* with the second and third persons.

I *will* go. (MEANS: I am positively determined to go.)

He *shall* settle the matter. (MEANS: Someone is definitely going to settle the matter.)

In these sentences, the speaker emphasized *will* and *shall* strongly. They are an example of the *determined* future.

The *simple* future—*shall* with the first person and *will* with the second and third persons—is used far more often than the *determined* future.

PRACTICE. In these blanks, fill in the proper *past tense* and *future tense* forms of the verb used in the sentences at left.

Present	Past	Future
1. I appoint.	He _____	We _____
2. He carries.	You _____	They _____
3. They remit.	She _____	They _____
4. It refers.	They _____	You _____
5. He wishes.	You _____	We _____

Insert the correct helping verb, **shall** or **will**, in each of these sentences.

6. We _____ be glad to hear from you.

7. We _____ positively do everything we can to please you.

8. I believe that the goods _____ reach Cedar Rapids tomorrow.

9. Nothing _____ make me swerve from my duty.

10. You may be absolutely sure that we _____ do everything we can to stay on schedule.

Secondary tenses. So far you have read about the *primary* tenses of verbs: present, past, and future. Here are the *secondary* tenses:

TENSE	MEANING	HELPING VERB	EXAMPLE
perfect	action begun in the past and completed in the present	have (has)	We have complied.
past perfect	action begun in the past and completed in the past	had	We had complied.
future perfect	action begun in the past to be completed in the future	shall (will) have	We shall have complied.

Perfect tense confusion. In the perfect tense, the helping verb *have* is often confused with the word *of* in contracted constructions using *would* and *should*.

I **should have** gone.
I **should've** gone.
NOT: I should *of* gone.

I **would have** done it yesterday.
I **would've** done it yesterday.
NOT: I would *of* done it yesterday.

This mistake arises from the similar sounds produced in pronouncing *should've* and *should of*. In writing, the careless pronunciation must be clarified by writing the correct words.

Emphatic tense forms. The emphatic tense forms are used for special stress emphasis. These tenses employ *do* or *did* followed by the infinitive form of the verb without the word *to*. Using the verb *to study* as an example, here are some examples of the emphatic tense.

I **do** study every night. (present)
I **did** study every night in college. (past)

Emphatic forms are used only in the present and past tenses of the active voice of the verb, never in the passive voice.

PRESENT	PAST
He **does** reply.	He **did** reply.
He **doesn't** reply.	He **didn't** reply.

PRACTICE. Fill in the blanks with the proper form of the verb used in the present tense.

Present	Perfect	Past Perfect
1. She omits.	She _____	I _____
2. It stays.	He _____	They _____
3. He applies.	It _____	You _____
4. We reply.	She _____	They _____
5. You refer.	They _____	We _____

Fill in the word **don't** or **doesn't** to complete the sentence correctly.

6. He surely _____ believe that he can succeed.

7. That man's word _____ carry any weight with me.

8. They _____ deserve all the blame.

9. It _____ occur every day.

UNIT 6 ▽ APPLICATION
Verbs and Their Tenses

Fill in the correct past tense and future tense forms of the verb used in the sentences at left.

	Past	Future	For Scoring
1. I travel.	He _____.	We _____.	_____
2. Ocean liners carry travelers.	Ocean liners _____ travelers.	Ocean liners _____ travelers.	_____
3. Jet airliners transport people more rapidly.	Jet airliners _____ people more rapidly.	Jet airliners _____ people more rapidly.	_____
4. Helicopters fly mail on short runs from airports to cities.	Helicopters _____ mail on short runs from airports to cities.	Helicopters _____ mail on short runs from airports to cities.	_____
5. The automobile provides the most common means of transportation.	The automobile _____ the most common means of transportation.	The automobile _____ the most common means of transportation.	_____

Fill in **don't** or **doesn't** to complete these sentences.

6. Mr. Edwards _____ say on which train he is arriving. _____

7. A hardworking man _____ lack self-esteem. _____

8. It just _____ seem right to me. _____

9. If you _____ remember your lines, you can't play the scene. _____

10. It is plain that he _____ know what he is talking about. _____

11. I understand why he _____ like spinach. _____

12. It _____ make any difference to me. _____

13. He _____ think before he speaks. _____

14. They _____ understand the situation. _____

15. She _____ seem to be able to explain the problem. _____

Fill in the blanks with the proper form of the verb used in the present tense.

Present	Perfect	Past Perfect	
16. He replies.	He _____	You _____	_____
17. She remarks.	She _____	I _____	_____
18. It stays.	He _____	They _____	_____
19. He proves.	It _____	You _____	_____
20. She applies.	He _____	They _____	_____

Fill in the blanks with the future perfect form of the verb given in the present tense.

21. He surrenders.   He _____ _____

22. She specifies.   She _____ _____

23. He signs.   He _____ _____

24. They object.   They _____ _____

25. I understand.   I _____ _____

UNITS 4–6 ▽ RECAP

Pronouns and Antecedents ▽ Verbs and Their Tenses

Here are the highlights of the guides relating to pronouns and their antecedents, and verbs and their past tense, future tense, and secondary tenses.

The pronoun. A pronoun is a word used in place of a noun. Pronouns have person, gender, and number.

Antecedent. The word the pronoun takes the place of is called the antecedent of that pronoun. The antecedent determines the person, gender, and number of the pronoun.

Verbs. A verb is a word that shows action or state. A complete thought cannot be conveyed without using a verb.

Tense. Tense is used to refer to the *time* shown by the verb. There are three primary tenses: present, past, and future.

Formation of third person singular of a verb. Most verbs add *s* to form the third person singular. The exceptions to this rule must be learned.

Formation of the past tense of regular verbs. The regular way to form the past tense of a verb is to add *ed.* Exceptions to this rule must be learned.

Formation of future tense. Verbs form the future tense with the helping verbs *will* and *shall.*

Secondary tenses. The secondary tenses of verbs are the perfect, past perfect, and future perfect.

Perfect tense. The perfect tense is used to express action begun at some indefinite time in the past and completed in the present. Use *have* or *has* to form the perfect tense.

Past perfect tense. The past perfect tense is used to express action begun in the past and completed at a later time in the past. Use *had* to form the past perfect tense.

Future perfect tense. The future perfect tense expresses action begun in the past and to be completed in the future. Use *shall have* or *will have* to form the future perfect tense.

Read the example sentences below to determine which correctly illustrates the guide indicated. Write the letter of the correct sentence in the blank at the right.

For
Scoring

1. Formation of past tense—regular verbs.
   a. She knowed that he loved her.
   b. They walked to the store.

_____ _____

2. Pronoun and antecedent.
   a. Nobody knows what the future holds in store for him.
   b. Nobody knows what the future holds in store for them. _____ _____

3. Verb to show complete thought.
   a. The one who felt strongly about it.
   b. If he had realized she felt that way, he would have left. _____ _____

4. Future perfect tense.
   a. I shall have visited you by then.
   b. I shall see you tomorrow. _____ _____

5. Past perfect tense.
   a. You purchased it last week.
   b. You had purchased it by then. _____ _____

6. Perfect tense.
   a. I have swum in the ocean many times.
   b. I had swum in the ocean before I was ten years old. _____ _____

7. Present tense.
   a. The teacher stresses the importance of studying.
   b. The teacher stressing the importance of studying. _____ _____

8. Future tense
   a. You will have seen me by tomorrow.
   b. I shall see you tomorrow. _____ _____

9. Past tense.
   a. They obeyed the traffic rules.
   b. They had obeyed the traffic rules. _____ _____

10. Pronoun and antecedent.
    a. Every woman in the club is doing her share of the work.
    b. Every woman in the club are doing their share of the work. _____ _____

In the following sentences, underline the correct form of the words in parentheses.

11. The mayor said that (she, they) would do it herself. _____

12. A person cannot go on a long trip unless (he or she, they) is organized. _____

13. He and Jane (was, were) rowing the boat. _____

14. A person is rated by the quality of (her, their) performance. _____

15. He (trys, tries) to drive carefully. _____

16. A child often (echos, echoes) her mother's ideas. _____

17. He (refer, referred) the matter to his supervisor. _____

18. They often (obtained, obtainned) their supplies from us. _____

19. He is determined that he (shall, will) do it. _____

20. When asked whether she would help, she strongly replied, "I (will, shall)." _____

UNIT 7
Irregular Verbs

Many verbs form their past tense and perfect tense altogether irregularly. Thus, they are called irregular verbs. The correct forms must be learned by study and by observation of good writing, as there are no rules to follow. It is suggested that these forms be memorized.

Because the forms of the verbs *be* and *do* are used with the irregular verbs, it is important to review these also.

The forms in parentheses are called negative forms, i.e., a word which carries with it the idea of *not* or *no*. Notice that the negative forms are all contracted, except *am not*. The *o* in *not* is omitted in all these contracted forms, and that omission must be shown by putting in an apostrophe.

Present	Past	Perfect
I am (am not)	I was (wasn't)	I have (haven't) been
You are (aren't)	You were (weren't)	You have (haven't) been
He, she, it is (isn't)	He, she, it was (wasn't)	He, she, it has (hasn't) been
I do (don't)	I did (didn't)	I have (haven't) done
You do (don't)	You did (didn't)	You have (haven't) done
He, she, it does (doesn't)	He, she, it did (didn't)	He, she, it has (hasn't) done

PRACTICE. Fill in the proper *negative* (contracted) form of the verbs **be** or **do**, using the tense given in parentheses at the end of each sentence. Example: She _____ here when I left. (past) Answer: She *wasn't* here when I left.

1. I _____ going. (present)

2. I _____ finish the lesson. (past)

3. He _____ know what he should do. (present)

4. You _____ your work properly. (perfect)

5. She _____ have a chance at all. (past)

6. I _____ believe you know what to do. (present)

7. He _____ the crossword a single day this week. (perfect)

8. You _____ joking, were you? (past)

   Fill in the proper *affirmative* form of the verbs **be** or **do**, using the tense given in parentheses.

9. I _____ the very best I could. (past)

10. The company _____ the work to our satisfaction. (perfect)

11. It _____ me a lot of good to know that she _____ working hard. (present)

12. I am sure your study _____ you a world of good. (perfect)

13. You _____ exactly right. (past)

Listed below are some groups of common irregular verbs.

Group 1

Present	Past	Perfect
He breaks	broke	has broken
She chooses	chose	has chosen
You forget	forgot	have forgotten
It freezes	froze	has frozen
He speaks	spoke	has spoken
They swear	swore	have sworn
It tears	tore	has torn
They weave	wove	have woven
We win	won	have won

Group 2

I arise	arose	have arisen
You drive	drove	have driven
He rides	rode	has ridden
I write	wrote	have written
They underwrite	underwrote	have underwritten

Group 3

I bring	brought	have brought
He buys	bought	has bought
He catches	caught	has caught
They fight	fought	have fought

Group 4

He blows	blew	has blown
It draws	drew	has drawn
He flies	flew	has flown
You know	knew	have known

Group 5

He drinks	drank	has drunk
It rings	rang	has rung
She sings	sang	has sung
He springs	sprang	has sprung
It shrinks	shrank	has shrunk
I swim	swam	have swum

PRACTICE. Fill in the proper forms of the verbs used in the present tense. Use the simple future form.

Present	Past	Future	Perfect
1. He chooses.	They _____	I _____	She _____
2. We win.	I _____	You _____	He _____
3. I speak.	He _____	We _____	He _____
4. She writes.	They _____	I _____	He _____
5. He forgets.	I _____	You _____	She _____
6. She draws.	I _____	They _____	He _____

UNIT 7 ▽ APPLICATION
Irregular Verbs

Fill in the proper forms of the verbs used in the present tense. Use the simple future form.

For Scoring

Present	Past	Future	Perfect	
1. I swim.	We _____	They _____	She _____	_____
2. They throw.	He _____	You _____	He _____	_____
3. She sings.	He _____	I _____	We _____	_____
4. It blows.	He _____	We _____	You _____	_____
5. They shrink.	You _____	She _____	We _____	_____
6. It freezes.	They _____	They _____	It _____	_____
7. She arises.	We _____	I _____	He _____	_____
8. You ride.	He _____	We _____	She _____	_____
9. I tear.	You _____	He _____	We _____	_____
10. He weaves.	They _____	I _____	She _____	_____

In the following sentences, supply the correct form of the verb printed in parentheses.

11. Last year Esther Paramus (weave) a beautiful tapestry in commemoration of the association's centennial. _____ ____

12. Students too often believe they are already familiar with what needs to be (know) about using the telephone. _____ ____

13. They fail to realize that they (be) using the telephone for casual conversation rather than for business. _____ ____

14. Students who (know) the experience of being put off by poorly trained receptionists should learn from those experiences. _____ ____

15. Today there are many different types of telephone equipment that (negative be) available years ago. _____ ____

16. Call forwarding, callback, conference calls, and transfer calls have been (know) only in recent years.   _____ _____

17. Such new equipment as speakerphones, cord and cordless switchboards, mobile phones, and card dialers have also (spring) into use.   _____ _____

18. New importance has been (win) by special services such as WATS, tie lines, collect calls, and credit card calls.   _____ _____

19. An employee who (choose) to be an asset to her office must be aware of the basics in the telecommunications area.   _____ _____

20. A need for in-class activities to acquaint students with these basics has definitely (arise).   _____ _____

21. The student should also be responsible for ordinary politeness once the phone has (ring).   _____ _____

22. If he (speak) courteously in all situations, the employee can make the customer enjoy dealing with the company.   _____ _____

23. Students who have (shrink) from learning telephone techniques may become a hindrance to safety during emergencies.   _____ _____

24. Those who have (know) how to handle problem situations on the telephone have often saved the day.   _____ _____

25. Experience in using various types of equipment, screening calls, and being courteous as well as competent (draw) an employer's praise and gratitude to the employee.   _____ _____

UNIT 8
Irregular Verbs

The following groups contain more verbs which form their past and perfect tenses irregularly. They are best learned by study and usage.

Group 6

Present	Past	Perfect
He falls	fell	has fallen
I forgive	forgave	have forgiven
You give	gave	have given
He eats	ate	has eaten
It runs	ran	has run
It overruns	overran	has overrun

Group 7

She keeps	kept	has kept
You meet	met	have met
He reads	read	has read
She sweeps	swept	has swept
You send	sent	have sent
They lead	led	have led
We hear	heard	have heard
He leaves	left	has left
He deals	dealt	has dealt

Group 8

You shoot	shot	have shot
He loses	lost	has lost
We sell	sold	have sold
I tell	told	have told
We find	found	have found

PRACTICE. Fill in the proper forms of the verb used in the present tense. Use the simple future form.

Present	Past	Future	Perfect
1. You fall	She _____	I _____	He _____
2. She forgives	We _____	He _____	You _____
3. He eats	It _____	She _____	We _____
4. He keeps	We _____	I _____	You _____
5. I leave	You _____	He _____	She _____
6. You lead	They _____	She _____	We _____
7. She loses	You _____	I _____	He _____

Group 9

Present	Past	Perfect
He holds	held	has held
You build	built	have built
It becomes	became	has become
We stand	stood	have stood
He takes	took	has taken
She comes	came	has come
I mistake	mistook	have mistaken

Group 10

Present	Past	Perfect
He pays	paid	has paid
They overpay	overpaid	have overpaid
It makes	made	has made
He says	said	has said
It strikes	struck	has struck
They dig	dug	have dug

Group 11

Present	Past	Perfect
It bursts	burst	has burst
It costs	cost	has cost
He hits	hit	has hit
She puts	put	has put
He lets	let	has let
You shut	shut	have shut
We quit	quit	have quit
It hurts	hurt	has hurt

PRACTICE. Fill in the proper forms of the verb used in the present tense. Use the simple future form.

Present	Past	Future	Perfect
1. It hurts	It _____	It _____	It _____
2. He shuts	I _____	You _____	He _____
3. He overpays	We _____	You _____	We _____
4. She stands	I _____	We _____	He _____
5. It comes	We _____	I _____	You _____
6. It bursts	It _____	It _____	It _____
7. I quit	We _____	I _____	He _____
8. We let	You _____	I _____	He _____
9. He strikes	You _____	It _____	They _____
10. He puts	We _____	I _____	You _____

UNIT 8 ▽ APPLICATION

Irregular Verbs

Fill in the blanks in these sentences with the correct tense forms of the verbs given in parentheses.

For
Scoring

1. It _____ us far more than we expected to pay. (cost, past)   _____

2. I _____ altogether what you _____ . (mistake, past; say, past)   _____

3. He _____ himself when he _____ the door. (hurt, past; shut, past)   _____

4. He didn't succeed because he _____ too soon. (quit, past)   _____

5. They _____ only a little while when they _____ oil. (dig, past perfect; strike, past)   _____

6. Ms. Fulton _____ the bill when she _____ over the business. (pay, past; take, past)   _____

7. He _____ the ball just right. (hit, past)   _____

8. The boiler _____ three times, and the repairs _____ us eighty dollars. (burst, perfect; cost, perfect)   _____

9. The Wheeler Construction Company _____ many houses in this city. (build, perfect)   _____

10. She _____ her friend by the gossip. (hurt, past)   _____

11. He _____ from his horse yesterday. (fall, past)   _____

12. His wife _____ him first aid. (give, perfect)   _____

13. They _____ us many man-hours in lost time. (cost, perfect)   _____

14. All the students _____ in the cafeteria today. (eat, perfect)   _____

15. The expenses _____ higher than allowed for the budget. (run, perfect)   _____

16. I think she _____ interest all too quickly. (lose, present) _____

17. Our company _____ with Mr. Hallman for many years. (deal,

   perfect) _____

18. Mr. Henry _____ the opposition. (lead, past) _____

19. We _____ our factory because we _____ that we could buy

   the goods more cheaply than we could manufacture them. (sell, past; find,

   past) _____

20. Miss Mason _____ an hour ago. (leave, past) _____

21. I _____ that he _____ a good opportunity. (feel, present;

   lose, perfect) _____

22. I _____ Sir Oliver Lodge speak, and I _____ a number of

   his books. (hear, perfect; read, perfect) _____

23. He _____ me that he _____ you in Chicago. (tell, present;

   meet, past) _____

24. Our branch manager _____ me informed of the

   developments. (keep, perfect) _____

25. He _____ the booklet and _____ several additional

   copies. (read, past; send, past) _____

UNIT 9
Special Verbs

Lie and lay ▽
Rise and raise ▽
Sit, set, go, and see

The forms of the verbs *lie* and *lay*, and *rise* and *raise*, are so often confused that they need careful study in order that they may be used correctly.

Lie and lay. You can use these two irregular verbs correctly if you remember that *lie* is an *intransitive* verb and that *lay* is a *transitive* verb.

Present	Past	Perfect
He lies	lay	has lain
He lays	laid	has laid

The verb *lie* means to recline. There is, of course, another verb *lie*, which means to tell an untruth. There is no difficulty with the latter, however, because it is a regular verb.

He lies, he lied, he has lied

The verb *lie* that we are concerned with here is a condition verb. It doesn't take an object.

You *lie* down BUT you *lay* the book down

Most of the trouble arises from the fact that the past tense of *lie* is the same form as the present tense of *lay*.

Rise and raise. The same distinction exists between *rise* and *raise*. Notice that the latter is a regular verb. *Raise* is followed by an object on which the verb acts; *rise* is not followed by an object.

You *rise* in the morning BUT you *raise* the flag

Rise is an intransitive verb. It never takes an object. The principal parts of rise are *rise, rose,* and *risen.*

Raise is a transitive verb. It may take an object. As *raise* is a regular verb, its principal parts are *raise, raised,* and *raised.*

The price of wheat *rises*. (present tense)
The price of wheat *rose*. (past tense)
The price of wheat *has risen*. (present perfect tense)

He *raises* his hand. (present tense)
He *raised* his hand. (past tense)
He *has raised* his hand. (present perfect tense)

PRACTICE. Fill in the correct forms of the verb used in the column at left. In all cases, the verb lie means to recline.

Present	Past	Future	Perfect
1. I lie	She _____	You _____	It _____
2. They lay	He _____	I _____	You _____
3. It lies	It _____	She _____	They _____
4. You lie	We _____	It _____	We _____
5. He lays	You _____	They _____	I _____
6. She lies	He _____	We _____	He _____
7. He rises	She _____	We _____	He _____
8. We raise	He _____	I _____	It _____
9. We lie	It _____	They _____	She _____
10. I rise	We _____	It _____	She _____

Sit, set, go, and see. Four other verbs often used incorrectly are *sit* and *set*, and *go* and *see*.

Study these forms.

Present	Past	Perfect
He sits	sat	has sat
He sets	set	has set

Present	Past	Perfect
He goes	went	has gone
She sees	saw	has seen

Like the irregular verbs in Group 11, Unit 7, *set* has the same form in the present, past, and perfect. It is an action verb and is followed by an object.

You set the chair in the corner BUT you sit down on it

Set means to place or to put. *Sit*, however, is a condition verb and is never followed by an object.

Sit is an intransitive verb. It never takes an object. The principal parts of *sit* are *sit*, *sat*, and *sat*.

Set is a transitive verb. The principal parts are *set*, *set*, and *set*.

He sits on a chair. (present tense)
He sat on a chair. (past tense)
He has often sat there. (perfect tense)

He sets a time for the meeting. (present tense)
He set a time for the meeting. (past tense)
He has set a time for the meeting. (perfect tense)

Remember the forms of *go*. They are important in correct English usage.

**I go
I went
I have gone
You have gone
He has gone**

Never use *I have went* or *he has went*.

The forms of *see* are often misused. Never say *I seen*. The correct forms are:

I saw, you saw, he saw

PRACTICE. Fill in the correct forms of the verbs in the column at left.

Present	Past	Future	Perfect
1. He sits	She _____	We _____	You _____
2. You see	We _____	I _____	They _____
3. She sets	He _____	You _____	I _____
4. He goes	We _____	I _____	He _____
5. We sit	She _____	They _____	She _____
6. It goes	You _____	They _____	It _____
7. He sees	I _____	They _____	She _____
8. You see	I _____	We _____	They _____
9. He sets	You _____	I _____	You _____
10. They see	We _____	I _____	You _____
11. It sets	I _____	You _____	I _____
12. We go	I _____	She _____	You _____

UNIT 9 ▽ APPLICATION

Special Verbs

Fill in the correct form of the verb given in parentheses at the end of each sentence.

For
Scoring

1. I _____ you yesterday afternoon. (see - past) _____

2. A lazy man _____ in bed in the morning. (lie - present) _____

3. As soon as we _____ the advertisement in the paper, we

   _____ to the store. (see - past; go - past) _____

4. His discussion _____ a good many doubts in my mind. (raise -

   perfect) _____

5. The stock _____ to an all-time high. (rise - past) _____

6. We _____ in front of the fire for a long time. (sit - perfect) _____

7. We _____ March 15 as the date of our opening. (set - perfect) _____

8. She _____ the money on the counter. (lay - past) _____

9. In his speech, the president _____ down certain general

   principles. (lay - past) _____

10. With the aid of a derrick, they soon _____ the car from the

    tracks. (raise - past) _____

11. We _____ to that convention regularly each year. (go - perfect) _____

12. The executive committee _____ the date for the meeting. (set -

    present) _____

13. Mr. Martin said that he _____ no reason for such a change. (see -

    past) _____

14. He _____ on his chair all day and _____ type for campaign

    publications. (sit - present; set - present) _____

15. Although she _____ to Columbia University in her last two years of

    college, she _____ to a small college at home for the first two

    years. (go - perfect; go - past) _____

16. Since he made that statement, he _____ greatly in my

    estimation. (rise - perfect)   _____

17. We feel that we _____ a firm foundation on which to build. (lay -

    perfect)   _____

18. He _____ to great heights in his profession. (rise - past)   _____

19. I _____ this play on two other occasions. (see - perfect)   _____

20. They still _____ to the same store they _____ to for many

    years. (go - present; go - perfect)   _____

    In the following sentences, underline the correct form of the verb.

21. Because of satellite services, businesses (have raised, have rised) the number

    of independent communications systems.   _____

22. These new telecommunications services (have sat, have set) the possibility of

    replacing less efficient and more expensive systems.   _____

23. The advantages to the companies (lie, lies) in boosting their capacity to

    transmit their own telephone calls, data, and other forms of information.   _____

24. New services such as high-speed data communications and video-

    conferencing (go, goes) far ahead of the growth of conventional telephone

    services.   _____

25. Marketing specialists around the country (have saw, have seen) the advan-

    tages of these alternative communications systems.   _____

UNITS 7–9 ▽ RECAP

Irregular Verbs ▽ Special Verbs

Here are the highlights of the guides relating to irregular verbs and special verbs.

Irregular verbs. Irregular verbs form their past and perfect tenses altogether irregularly.

The perfect form. Remember that the perfect form of the verb is also used to form the present perfect, past perfect, and future perfect tenses.

To be and *to do.* Forms of these verbs are used with irregular verbs.

Read the sentences below to determine which correctly illustrates the guide indicated. Write the letter of the correct choice in the blank at the right.

For
Scoring

1. Correct use of *rise* or *raise*.
   a. He has raised the flag.
   b. He has risen the flag.   ____ ____

2. Correct use of *lie* or *lay*.
   a. Albert has laid down to rest.
   b. Albert has lain down to rest.   ____ ____

3. Correct use of *sit* or *set*.
   a. Mother has sat the table for dinner.
   b. Mother has set the table for dinner.   ____ ____

4. Correct use of *go*.
   a. He has gone to the baseball game.
   b. He has went to the baseball game.   ____ ____

5. Correct use of *see*.
   a. She has saw the movie twice.
   b. She has seen the movie twice.   ____ ____

For the following sentences, write the correct form of the verb in the blank at the right.

6. The star athlete (has broke, has broken) his leg.   _____ ____

7. She (choosed, chose) to attend a private school.   _____ ____

8. That little boy (has tore, has torn) his sweater twice today. _____ _____

9. The two men (has froze, have frozen) all the fish they caught. _____ _____

10. Our teacher (has spoke, has spoken) to our class about our noise before. _____ _____

11. They always (brought, brung) the bikes with them. _____ _____

12. After the bell (has rung, has rang), the students rush for the buses. _____ _____

13. All the golfers (have drove, have driven) their opening shots to the green. _____ _____

14. He never (has forgiven, has forgave) her for breaking their engagement. _____ _____

15. Mr. Quinn (builded, built) a swimming pool in his yard. _____ _____

16. When the balloon (burst, bursted), the little girl cried and asked for another one. _____ _____

17. I don't know how much his car (cost, costed). _____ _____

18. Because the team (has losed, has lost) the championship, the coach has resigned. _____ _____

19. When he (lays, lies) down to rest, the dog always jumps on the bed. _____ _____

20. She never (saw, seen) a prettier rainbow than that one. _____ _____

UNIT 10
Agreement of Subject and Predicate

The predicate (verb) of a sentence must agree in person and number with the subject of the sentence. If the subject is *third person singular*, for example, the verb must be *third person singular*.

Always look for the simple subject of the sentence and make the verb agree with it in *number*. Disregard the number of any word or words that come between the subject and the verb.

A good supply of automobile parts and accessories is kept in stock.

Parts and *accessories* are plural; but *supply*, the simple subject, is singular. It takes a singular predicate *is*.

Does (*doesn't*), *is* (*isn't*), and *has* (*hasn't*) are third person singular forms. *Do* (*don't*), *are* (*aren't*), and *have* (*haven't*) are third person plural forms.

A phrase that begins with *in addition to, together with*, or *as well as* doesn't affect the number of the subject.

The president, together with the members of the cabinet, was present at the discussion.

When the subject consists of two or more third person singular subjects joined by *or* or *nor*, the verb must be *singular*.

Either Mr. Galliano or Mr. Pappas has made this mistake.

Neither this office nor the Chicago office has filled an order for you.

These words are all singular: *one, anyone, someone, everyone, somebody, everybody, each, either, neither, nobody, no one*. Each one of these words used as a subject must take a singular verb.

Neither of the students *has* a pencil.

The indefinite pronouns *anyone, everyone, anything*, etc., are written as one word unless they are followed by a phrase beginning with *of*. In those cases, they are written as two separate words and still take a singular verb.

Every one of the choir members has had a cold.

Everybody was sick with the flu this year.

PRACTICE. Underline the correct verb in the parentheses.

1. Either Mr. Henry or his personal aide (have, has) investigated the matter.

2. The working schedule of our three factories (is, are) the same.

3. This whole matter, together with all the notes, (has, have) been referred to the vice-president.

4. This question of rates and custom duties (seems, seem) to cause a lot of trouble.

5. Neither Mr. Bernstein nor Mr. Anderson (is, are) the man you want.

6. Each of the men usually (come, comes) at nine o'clock.

7. Every one of the packages (contains, contain) a complete set.

8. Not one of all these papers (has, have) the information.

9. He (don't, doesn't) agree to the plan.

When the subject consists of two or more words joined by *and*, the verb must be plural.

A telegram and letter were sent.

The general and his staff have reviewed the regiment.

If one subject is singular and the other subject plural, place the plural subject last and make the verb plural. Follow this practice when the connecting word is *and*, *or*, or *nor*.

Either Mr. Johnson or his branch managers are responsible for this ruling.

Neither Kevin nor the girls have the answer to the problem.

Singular nouns such as *jury, committee, crowd, army*, and *class* are called *collective nouns* because they mean a collection of persons. When the subject of a sentence is a collective noun thought of as one whole, use the singular verb form.

The yearbook committee is the best in the school right now.

The crowd is the largest to attend a baseball game.

But if you are thinking of the individuals that make up the whole, use the plural verb.

The committee have disagreed among themselves.

The jury have not decided on a verdict.

Used as the subject of a sentence, the word *number* preceded by *the* takes a singular verb.

The number of strikers is growing.

The number of people present was 500.

However, when preceded by *a*, the word *number* takes a plural verb.

A number of men have already left work.

A number of the officers were present at the meeting.

When a noun that is plural in form is used to name a unit that is the title of a book or a sum of money, use a singular verb.

Alice's Adventures in Wonderland is a children's classic.

Two hundred dollars is too much.

PRACTICE. Underline the correct verb in the parentheses.

---

1. The high value and unusual merit of this new plan (is, are) perfectly clear.

2. Either the conductor or one of his musicians (is, are) responsible.

3. Money, as well as men and machines, (is, are) needed.

4. Your approach and opening statement (was, were) wrong.

5. The class in economics (meet, meets) every Wednesday at two o'clock.

6. The jury (disagree, disagrees) on the merits of the prosecutor's argument.

7. Ten thousand dollars (is, are) too much to pay.

8. A crowd of angry people (is, are) hard to control.

9. A large number of workmen (has, have) been injured.

10. The number (was, were) highly exaggerated in the newspapers.

11. Neither the king nor his subjects (are, is) in danger.

12. The Belgian army (is, are) on maneuvers near Brussels.

UNIT 10 ▽ APPLICATION

Agreement of Subject and Predicate

Underline the correct word in the parentheses.

1. Either of the machines (are, is) suitable for this work. _____

2. A number of new offices (has, have) been opened recently. _____

3. The number of errors in our shipments (seems, seem) to be growing. _____

4. Action, not words, (is, are) what we want. _____

5. The jury (begin, begins) consideration of the case this afternoon. _____

6. Not one of those gentlemen (was, were) present at the meeting. _____

7. Neither Mr. Feuer nor his representative (know, knows) what happened. _____

8. In addition to his report, his cost analysis (were, was) excellent. _____

9. Training and experience (is, are) both necessary for real success. _____

10. Everybody in the organization (has, have) done the best he could. _____

11. This question of rates and discounts (cause, causes) a lot of difficulty. _____

12. A great variety of shoes and clothes (was, were) offered for sale. _____

13. The spirit behind the mottoes (are, is) what I like. _____

14. *The Adventures of Huckleberry Finn* (is, are) a classic. _____

15. The company (start, starts) operations in its new plant next Monday. _____

16. The sales managers as well as the president (deserve, deserves) a good
    share of praise. _____

17. When the subject of a sentence consists of two or more third person
    singular subjects joined by *or* or *nor*, the verb must be (singular, plural). _____

18. When the subject consists of *two* or more nouns, representing different
    persons or objects, joined by *and*, the verb is (singular, plural). _____

19. Forty-five cents above cost (is, are) not enough margin to make a profit. _____

20. Every one of the new team members (have, has) made good. _____

In the following groups of sentences, write the letter of the one that is correct in the blank at the right.

21. a. Each of the packages seem to be opened.

    b. Either of these tires appears to be satisfactory.

    c. Accuracy in details mark the work of a good stenographer.

    d. The news about these plans have just reached me.   _____ _____

22. a. A telegram and a night letter was sent.

    b. Both communications said, "Action, not words, are what we

       want."

    c. Each of the managers agrees with this.

    d. Yet a number of the board members is angry about the

       communication.   _____ _____

23. a. Automation in offices is on the increase.

    b. A computerized word processor or electronic typewriter with

       videoscreen are basic equipment.

    c. A number of stations receives messages from the word

       processor.

    d. Computer technology in modern offices are fascinating.   _____ _____

24. a. Electronic typewriters with memory is becoming standard

       equipment.

    b. Line return and carrier return are two separate operations.

    c. A number of word processors has a pre-set grid.

    d. Form letters for mass mailing is prepared by merely changing

       the inside address and other variables.   _____ _____

25. a. There was six members on the committee.

    b. This committee are the best one that could be selected.

    c. Sometimes they agrees on everything that is discussed.

    d. At other times, the committee have disagreed among

       themselves.   _____ _____

UNIT 11
Cases of Nouns

Nominative ▽ Objective ▽ Possessive

Cases of nouns. Forms that indicate the way nouns and pronouns are used in sentences are called *case* forms. The case of a word indicates the grammatical meaning or sense relation of the word to another word or words in the sentence; therefore, case expresses different functions of words in the sentence. In English, there are three cases; *nominative* (also called *subjective*), *objective*, and *possessive*.

Nominative case. A noun is in the *nominative* (or *subjective*) *case* primarily when it acts as the *subject of a verb*.

The *wagon* rolled down the hill.

The easiest way to determine the subject of the verb is to ask *who* or *what* is doing the action. In the sentence above, *the wagon* rolled down the hill. Therefore, *wagon* is the subject.

The nominative case is also used for the *predicate nominative* and the *appositive*. A noun is an appositive of another noun when it identifies the same person or object under another name (see Unit 12).

Connie, the group leader, called a meeting for today.

Objective case. A noun is in the objective case when it acts as the object of a verb—direct or indirect—or as the object of a preposition.

Direct Object of a Verb. By asking *whom* or *what* after the verb, you can identify the word functioning as a direct object.

Alice saw the *lake*.

What did Alice see? The *lake. Lake* is the direct object of the verb *saw*.

Indirect Object. By asking *to whom, to what, for whom,* or *for what* the action of the verb is performed, you can identify the indirect object. The indirect object usually comes before the direct object.

The teacher gave *Albert* the ball.

To whom did the teacher give the ball? To *Albert. Albert* is the indirect object.

Object of a Preposition. The word following the preposition is normally its object.

The dog sat under the *porch*.

Porch is the object of the preposition *under*. Prepositions and their objects are further explained in Unit 17.

Some commonly used prepositions are *in, over, around, between, down,* and *among*.

PRACTICE. In the following sentences, the italicized nouns are all in the nominative case. Identify their use in the sentences as **SV** for a subject of a verb, **PN** for a predicate nominative, or **APP** for an appositive. Write your answer in the blanks at right.

1. Billy, *the pitcher*, threw a curveball. _____

2. *Agnes Potemich* constructed a wall of stones around the

   garden. _____

3. The best actor was *Hilary*. _____

4. After finishing college, *Robert* went into business for

   himself. _____

5. During the service, Reverend Miller, *the preacher*,

   delivered an eloquent sermon. _____

Possessive case.

Although the *nominative* and *objective* cases of nouns are together called the *common case* because these nouns are spelled alike, the *possessive case* form of the noun is always spelled differently because of the use of the apostrophe. The apostrophe is called the sign of the possessive.

Forming the Possessive. These rules are simple and definite. You should learn their application thoroughly.

Singular nouns form the possessive by adding *'s*.

attorney, attorney's; lady, lady's

Plural nouns ending in *s* form the possessive by adding the apostrophe only.

allies, allies'; lawyers, lawyers'

Plural nouns ending in any other letter but *s* form the possessive by adding *'s*.

children, children's; women, women's

Add an apostrophe and *s* to form the possessive case of singular *proper nouns*, including those that end in *s*.

**Wells's *The Outline of History*
Dickens's plots**

In *compound nouns*, the singular compound noun is made possessive by adding *'s*.

**Her sister-in-law's recipe
The editor in chief's responsibility**

If a plural compound noun ends in *s*, make it possessive by adding the apostrophe only. Otherwise, add apostrophe *s*.

In *joint ownership*, only the last name is written with the apostrophe *s*.

Logan and Wilson's Store

In *separate ownership*, both names receive the apostrophe *s*.

We celebrated Betty's and Peggy's birthdays together.

In plural nouns that are official names of associations or organizations, the apostrophe is often omitted.

**Teachers College
Citizens Planning Association**

Certain proper nouns that end in *s* are written with just the apostrophe to form the possessive case.

**Jesus   Jesus' birth
Moses   Moses' laws**

PRACTICE. Fill in the blanks at the right of these sentences with the correct possessive form of the noun given in parentheses.

---

1. You will find a full line of our (company) products on sale at Harper's store. _____

2. The Southern (Manufacturer) Association will be the mayor's guest at lunch today. _____

3. My (brother) family consists of two girls and two boys. _____

4. The special sale on (woman) and children's dresses begins on Thursday morning. _____

5. Mr. Thompson's letter states that you will soon put in a complete line of (barber) supplies. _____

6. You will get more than three (months) wear out of those shoes. _____

UNIT 11 ▽ APPLICATION

Cases of Nouns

Rewrite these expressions in the blanks at right using the possessive of the second noun to show ownership.

For Scoring

1. The toy belonging to the child _____ _____

2. An association of teachers _____ _____

3. Dresses for ladies _____ _____

4. The business of the company _____ _____

5. A club of stenographers _____ _____

6. The duty of a secretary _____ _____

7. The case of the plaintiff _____ _____

8. Wages of workmen _____ _____

9. The mayor of the city _____ _____

10. A conference of salesmen _____ _____

Write the possessive of the words in parentheses in the blanks at right. Add other apostrophes where appropriate in each sentence.

11. Six (month) interest is now due

    on Mr. Butlers note. _____ _____

12. My (attorney) advice is to put in a

    bill for ten months interest. _____ _____

13. "We have crowded six weeks

    work into one week," the

    (treasurer) office wrote us. _____ _____

14. The auditors are now going over

    the (secretary) report to the

    trustees. _____ _____

15. Babies soft-soled shoes are sold

    only through our (company) retail

    stores. _____ _____

16. Statements are sent each month

    on (customer) accounts. _____ _____

17. My (attorney) advice is to push

    for settlement of the bill. _____ _____

18. The applicants English is so poor

    that I do not believe she could

    take the (manager) dictation. _____ _____

19. A (creditor) meeting will be held

    on Thursday to determine what

    action shall be taken in case of

    the firm's bankruptcy. _____ _____

20. Please give him three days pay

    for three (day) work. _____ _____

21. The (company) equipment gave out

    without a moment's notice. _____ _____

22. My (brother-in-law) store will have

    a one-day sale. _____ _____

In each question below, choose the sentence that contains the correct form of the possessive noun. Write the letter of that sentence in the blank at the right.

23. a. They also assist them in the analysis of any change in the price
       levels' effects.
    b. They also assist them in the analysis of any change in the price
       levels effects.
    c. They also assist them in the analysis of any change in the price
       levels effects'. _____ _____

24. a. Consequently, cost effectiveness is used to measure a
       proposals' advantages.
    b. Consequently, cost effectiveness is used to measure a
       proposals advantages'.
    c. Consequently, cost effectiveness is used to measure a
       proposal's advantages. _____ _____

25. a. Todays accounting strategies' for inflation are often misleading
       and incomplete.
    b. Today's accounting strategies for inflation are often misleading
       and incomplete.
    c. Todays' accounting strategies for inflation are often misleading
       and incomplete. _____ _____

UNIT 12
Cases of Pronouns

Nominative case ▽
Possessive case

Like nouns, pronouns have three cases: *nominative*, *possessive*, and *objective* (see Unit 13). These forms depend on how pronouns are used in sentences.

She went to the store. (nominative)
I gave her a book. (objective)
The green dress is hers. (possessive)

Although a pronoun agrees with its antecedent in number, person, and gender, it does not necessarily agree in case. Notice the pronouns in the following sentence:

Bill called Alice; she did not call him.

Bill is in the nominative case, but *him*, the pronoun that takes the place of *Bill*, is in the objective case. On the other hand, *Alice* is an objective case noun, but the pronoun *she* that takes the place of *Alice* is in the nominative case. The case of the pronoun is determined by its function in the sentence.

Nominative case. The *nominative* or *subjective case* of the pronoun indicates that the pronoun acts as a subject. There are three uses of the nominative case of the pronoun.

It can be used as the subject of a sentence.

She went to college.
He and I are married.
Neither she nor he has arrived.

It can be used as an appositive of the subject of a sentence.

Two students, she and I, hope to get tuition loans.

It can also be used as a *predicate complement*. A pronoun is a predicate complement when it is joined to the subject of the sentence by a form of *be* as a linking verb: *is, are, was, were, has been, will be*, etc. This kind of predicate complement is called the *predicate nominative*.

The winner of the prize was she.
It was he.
The best skaters are he and they.

Because the predicate nominative means the same thing as the subject, we can turn it around without changing the meaning of the sentence. In the examples above, the sentences can be rewritten as follows.

She was the winner of the prize.
He was it.
He and they are the best skaters.

Note that in both sets of sentences, the same pronoun forms are used when the pronouns are the *subjects* of the sentences.

When a sentence has two subjects joined by *and, or,* or *nor,* and the second subject is a pronoun, the pronoun must be in the nominative case.

Neither my friend nor I can go.
You and he should be able to go.

PRACTICE. Identify the uses of the nominative case of the pronoun in these sentences as **S** for subject of a sentence, **A** for appositive of the subject of the sentence, or **PN** for predicate nominative. Write your answers in the blanks at right.

1. The Olympic medalists are *he and she*. _____

2. *They* arrived home from their trip a week late. _____

3. Both sides, *we and they*, have been awarded prizes. _____

4. The teacher who failed him is *I*. _____

5. *We* hiked in the state park for a week. _____

Possessive case. Pronouns have special forms for their possessives. Notice that *no* possessive form of any pronouns ending in *s* has an apostrophe.

That desk is *yours*.
The coats are *theirs*.
The hat is *hers*.
These books are *ours*.

Here are the various forms of the possessive case.

	SINGULAR POSSESSIVE	PLURAL POSSESSIVE
First Person	**my, mine**	**our, ours**
Second Person	**your, yours**	**your, yours**
Third Person	**his, hers**	**their, theirs**

Remember that a pronoun must agree with its antecedent in gender, person, and number.

Formerly, when the gender of the antecedent was not known, the masculine pronoun was used. Now the rule is that either masculine or feminine may be used.

Everyone should do *her* best all of the time.

Someone has left *his* notebook lying on the desk.

If there are two singular antecedents of different genders, the rule is to use two pronouns. You may *not* use *their* to refer to a singular antecedent.

Either a man or a woman will be accepted for the position, but his or her application must be filed in time.

A collective noun, you will remember, is the name given to a noun that means a number of objects or persons. Use the singular pronoun to refer to a *collective noun* when it is thought of as a single unit. However, when the individual members comprising the collective noun are emphasized, use the plural pronoun.

The jury has rendered its verdict.

The jury are now preparing to go home.

It is very important to remember that the possessive pronoun *its* never has an apostrophe. The apostrophe is used in *it's* only for the contraction of *it is* to show the omission of *i* in *is*.

In the same way, *you're* is a contraction for *you are*. The apostrophe shows the omission of *a* in *are*.

PRACTICE. Study the antecedent in each of these sentences and then fill in the blanks with the correct possessive pronoun.

---

1. After deliberating all night, the jury rendered _____ verdict.

2. Someone has done _____ best to spoil the work.

3. Each person has a right to _____ own likes and dislikes.

4. The school will celebrate _____ twentieth anniversary next week.

5. The company has contributed _____ share to the community fund.

6. Has everybody in class finished _____ assignment?

7. The class have not agreed on _____ representative to the education convention.

8. Let each member do _____ best to get at least one new member.

9. Almost every city and town has _____ own war memorial.

10. The Fulton estate has sold part of _____ holdings.

UNIT 12 ▽ APPLICATION

Cases of Pronouns

After checking the antecedent, underline the correct pronoun from the words in parentheses.

For
Scoring

1. The Baltimore and Ohio Railroad has celebrated (their, its) one hundredth

   anniversary.   ———

2. The principal of a school is (its, their) leader.   ———

3. No one can do (their, his or her) best work in an overheated room lacking

   proper ventilation.   ———

4. Either a man or a woman will win the race, but (they, he or she) will have

   to be in top form.   ———

5. If the brand-new car in the parking lot is (your's, yours), take good care of

   it.   ———

6. Nobody should ever do anything less than (their, his or her) very best in

   such a situation.   ———

7. "An army travels on (their, its) stomach," said Napoleon.   ———

8. The committee appointed last week is now selecting (their, its) chairman.   ———

9. I feel absolutely sure that everyone will perform (their, his or her) part as

   well.   ———

10. Economics is an important subject, since (their, its) value cannot be ques-

    tioned.   ———

11. Each company in the new industrial estate shows a large increase in (their,

    its) inventories.   ———

12. Neither of the girls has finished transcribing (their, her) notes on the nature

    trek.   ———

13. Nobody knows what (their, his or her) future holds in store.   ———

14. The reader of the story about the prince, the princess, and the frog was (her, she). _____

15. Tom and (him, he) went fishing today. _____

16. Two cheerleaders, Alice and (me, I), conducted the pep rally before the vital play-off game. _____

17. Neither John nor (me, I) can do the drills that we were taught last week in our gym class. _____

18. Gerry looked for Jim, but he did not find (he, him). _____

19. Mary borrows her sister's clothes, and sometimes her sister borrows (her's, hers). _____

20. That book which I found last week in the attic is not mine; it is (your's, yours). _____

21. Those geography books over there on the dining room table are (our's, ours). _____

22. The teacher said the books that they had bought last summer were (theirs, their's). _____

23. Either a student or a teacher will monitor the exam, but (he or she, they) must be screened. _____

24. The urban development company has just published (its, their) annual statement. _____

25. He does not agree that everybody is entitled to (their, his or her) own opinion. _____

UNIT 13
Objective Case of Pronouns

Objective pronouns and prepositions ▽ Appositives as objects of verbs ▽ Compound pronouns

Uses. There are many uses for the objective case of pronouns. One of the most common is to complete the meaning of an active transitive verb. We have seen that verbs show condition or action. The action verb which is followed by a word that completes its meaning is a *transitive verb*. The word that completes the meaning is the *direct object* of the verb.

I *taught her.*
He *hit him.*

These pronouns act as receivers of action and must be in the objective case because the action of the verb must be on an *object*. When that object is a noun, there should be no problem because a noun does not change form when it is in the objective case. However, the pronoun forms do change.

These are the objective forms of personal pronouns:

	Singular Objective	Plural Objective
First person	*me*	*us*
Second person	*you*	*you*
Third person	*him, her, it*	*them*

A *condition* verb does not show action on the object that follows; the condition verb simply carries over the thought from the subject to the word that follows. After condition verbs (forms of *be*), we have already seen that the regular or nominative forms of pronouns are used. Thus, we have the *noun* (or *pronoun*) *complement*, or *predicate nominative* as it is called.

It is *I*.

Confusing the nominative and objective forms of the pronouns can create confusion in the meaning of the sentence.

Robert loved Regina more than I.
Robert loved Regina more than me.

In the first sentence, Robert loved Regina more than *I* loved Regina. In the second sentence, Robert loved Regina more than *Robert* loved *me*.

The meaning of both sentences depends on words ordinarily left out of the sentences in making comparison.

Observe the following examples:

Subject–Nominative Form:

Mr. Waters can obtain an order faster than *he* (can obtain an order).
Mary asks more questions than *I* (ask).

Object–Objective Form:

That looks better on you than (it looks) on *her*.
Barry gave Tom more money than (he gave) *me*.

A common error is to say, "She is taller than me." If you supply the missing verb, you can see that this is incorrect. You would never say, "She is taller than me (am)."

PRACTICE. Fill in the blanks in these sentences with the correct pronoun forms. If both forms are correct, be prepared to explain why.

1. The person who called you on the phone was (her, she). _____

2. Anthony is taller than (me, I). _____

3. Adam loved her more than (I, me). _____

4. Betty plays more bridge than (I, me). _____

5. Mr. Thompson gave Sam more credit than (me, I). _____

Objective pronouns and prepositions.

A preposition is a word that shows relation between other words. Some common prepositions are *between, by, for, from, in, to, under,* and *above.* Frequently, prepositions relate pronouns to a word or other words in the sentence.

Mr. Jones gave the house to *them*.

In the sentence above, *to* is a preposition that relates the pronoun *them* to the word house.

The word that follows the preposition, in this instance the pronoun *them*, is called the object of the preposition. When pronouns are objects of prepositions, they must always be in the objective case.

When a preposition has two pronoun objects joined by *and* or *or*, both pronouns must be objective.

He gave it to *him* and *me*.
It will not matter to *him* or *her*.

The word *but* is a preposition when it means *except*. When a pronoun is the object of *but*, it must be in the objective case.

There is nobody here but *me*.

Pronouns are also in the objective case when used as indirect objects of verbs. An indirect object usually precedes the direct object and is written without the words "to" or "for."

She gave *him* a present.
He did *her* a favor.

Appositives as objects of verbs.

Pronouns that are used in apposition and that are objects of verbs must always be in the objective case.

I asked the neighbors, both *him* and *her*, to come to the wedding.

These are some important rules of pronoun usage:

When pronouns are used as subjects, nominative forms must be used.

She went to the park.

When pronouns are used after verbs that express condition, the nominative forms must be used.

It was *they* who lost the money.

When pronouns are used as objects of action verbs, the objective forms must be used.

She watches *him*.

Compound pronouns.

Pronouns can be made compound by adding *self* for the singular and *selves* for the plural.

myself, yourself, himself, herself, itself, yourselves, ourselves, themselves

These compound words are never split. Compound pronouns are made *intensive* when used after a noun or another pronoun for emphasis.

She herself made her prom gown.

The same pronouns are made *reflexive* when the pronouns *turn back to* or *reflect on* an action of the doer of the action.

She made herself a spinning wheel.

PRACTICE. Fill in the blanks with the correct form of the pronoun.

1. You may send Mr. Jackson or (I, me) to the conference. _____

2. There is a lot of tension between Ella and (he, him). _____

3. Neither the president nor (him, he) can make the convention. _____

4. All the contestants but (she, her) came from out of town. _____

5. Angelo presented (him, he) a raise for his efforts. _____

6. I asked (myself, mineself) many times why I did it. _____

7. The principal (hisself, himself) took a turn at cafeteria duty. _____

UNIT 13 ▽ APPLICATION

Objective Case of Pronouns

Fill in the blanks in these sentences with the correct pronoun forms according to the instructions in parentheses.

For
Scoring

1. It was clearly _____ who were in the wrong. (First person-plural) _____

2. I say frankly that it was _____ who was in the wrong. (First person-singular) _____

3. Yes, it was _____ all right. (Second person-singular) _____

4. It was _____ who directed the campaign. (Third person-singular-masculine) _____

5. If anybody can solve the problem, it is _____ . (Third person-singular-feminine) _____

6. In most cases, it has been _____ who have worked out the answer. (Third person-plural) _____

7. I had the books here, but now I have lost _____ . (Third person-plural) _____

8. I saw them plainly, and I am absolutely certain it was _____. (Third person-plural) _____

9. I shall oppose her at every point because I feel it is _____ who is in the wrong. (Third person-singular-feminine) _____

10. Poor knowledge of English cost _____ a good opportunity. (Third person-singular-masculine) _____

11. He doesn't remember whether he sent the books to Chicago or directly to _____ in New York. (second person-plural) _____

12. Letters of application were written by Mary and _____ . (Third person-singular-feminine) _____

13. There is nobody in the house but _____ . (First person-singular) _____

14. He is drawing up a set of specifications for the architect and _____ . (Third person-singular-masculine) _____

In the following sentences, underline the correct form of the pronoun in parentheses.

15. Clifton, the blond twin, is taller than (me, I). _____

16. She was more responsible than (I, me). _____

17. It must have been (her, she) that left the package here. _____

18. But for (him, he), the work would have been dropped long ago. _____

19. Martina is conducting the tour for Giles and (he, him). _____

20. Neither you nor (me, I) will make mistakes if we study the plan. _____

In the following groups of sentences, write the letter of the one that is correct in the blank at the right.

21. a. The language have its mysteries.

    b. Primitive cultures claim that language has its own magic.

    c. Words have they're own power.

    d. Some people forbid theirselfs the use of certain words. _____ _____

22. a. John can use language better than her.

    b. New words are needed to express new ideas of our's.

    c. Plato wanted to expel all poets from his ideal republic.

    d. He believed their power with words corrupted you and I. _____ _____

23. a. She sent a book of classical rhetoric for you and me to use.

    b. Techniques of language and it's use are explained in the book.

    c. A study of these techniques will profit he and she.

    d. Either him or her will improve their language skills. _____ _____

24. a. There is nobody to blame but I for ignoring good grammar.

    b. The advice given by the principal and she is to study hard.

    c. Tony hisself did not believe a study of rhetoric would help.

    d. John bought himself both a grammar book and a thesaurus. _____ _____

25. a. Alice and her went to ask for a review of the object of the preposition.

    b. It is him who needs more help.

    c. Neither your teacher nor I can stress too much the importance of grammar and rhetoric.

    d. It was them who were not persuaded of the value of language skills. _____ _____

UNITS 10–13 ▽ RECAP

Agreement of Subject and Predicate ▽
Cases of Nouns ▽
Cases of Pronouns

Here are the highlights of the guides relating to agreement of subject and predicate, and the nominative, possessive, and objective cases of nouns and pronouns.

Subject and predicate agreement. The predicate of a sentence must agree in person and number with the subject of the sentence.

Subject joined by *or* or *nor*. When the subject consists of two or more third person singular subjects joined by *or* or *nor*, the verb must be singular.

Collective nouns. Collective nouns are thought of as a whole and take a singular verb form. However, if the individuals in that group are thought of individually, a plural verb must be used.

Compound subject. One singular subject with one plural subject takes a plural verb.

Nominative case of nouns. Nouns are in the nominative (or subjective) case when used as subjects of verbs, as predicate nominatives, and as appositives.

Objective case of nouns. Nouns in the objective case are used as objects of verbs (direct or indirect) and as objects of prepositions.

Rules for forming the possessive of nouns. Singular nouns form the possessive by adding *'s*. Plural nouns ending in *s* form the possessive by adding the apostrophe only. Other plural nouns form the possessive by adding *'s*. Singular proper nouns, including those that end in *s*, form the possessive by adding *'s*. Plural proper nouns add the apostrophe only.

Forms of possessive pronouns. No possessive form of any pronoun ending in *s* has an apostrophe.

Objective case of pronouns. Pronouns used to complete the meaning of action verbs are objective in form.

Pronouns with condition verbs. Such pronouns do not show action on the object that follows. Since *be* is the principal condition verb, the nominative pronouns *I*, *he*, *she*, *we*, and *they* must be used. This is called the predicate nominative.

Read the example sentences below to determine which correctly illustrates the guide. Write the letter of the correct choice in the blank at the right.

For Scoring

1. Subject and predicate agreement.
   a. The course offerings of our school is excellent.
   b. The course offerings of our school are excellent.   _____ _____

2. Subject joined by *or* or *nor*.
   a. Neither his mother nor his father is attending the wedding.
   b. Neither his mother nor his father are attending the wedding. _____ _____

3. Collective nouns taking a singular verb form.
   a. The jury has come to its decision after ten hours of debate.
   b. The jury have come to its decision after ten hours of debate. _____ _____

4. Possessive of singular nouns.
   a. All the players owned that team's equipment.
   b. All the players owned that teams' equipment. _____ _____

5. Possessive of plural nouns ending in *s*.
   a. The men gathered in the community bricklayer's hall.
   b. The men gathered in the community bricklayers' hall. _____ _____

6. Possessive of plural nouns not ending in *s*.
   a. They suggested that a womens' club be formed.
   b. They suggested that a women's club be formed. _____ _____

7. Possessive of singular proper noun ending in *s*.
   a. That is Mr. Mill's property.
   b. That is Mr. Mills's property. _____ _____

8. Possessive pronouns ending in *s*.
   a. The responsibility for the problem is their's.
   b. The responsibility for the problem is theirs. _____ _____

9. Noun as object of preposition.
   a. The audience sat there spellbound.
   b. The audience sat spellbound in the theater. _____ _____

10. Pronoun as indirect object of verb.
    a. Sally gave he a beautiful gift.
    b. Sally gave him a beautiful gift. _____ _____

For the following sentences, write the correct form of the words
in parentheses in the blanks at right.

11. There is nobody going to the play but (me, I). _____ _____

12. Either Sally or (she, her) will lead the cheers. _____ _____

13. But for (her, she), the team would lose its spirit. _____ _____

14. That is a matter between you and (me, I). _____ _____

15. Hildegard saw all the (girls', girl's) coats on the floor. _____ _____

16. All the members of the club decided that (their, its) votes
    were important. _____ _____

17. Shirley argued that the choice was (hers, her's). _____ _____

18. It was (him, he) who started the fuss. _____ _____

19. He recognized the importance of (Moses', Moses's) laws. _____ _____

20. The high standards and careful work of the employee (was,
    were) praised. _____ _____

UNIT 14
Adjectives

Kinds of adjectives ▽
Forms of adjectives ▽
Predicate adjectives ▽
Adjective clauses

Adjectives. An adjective is a word that modifies a noun or a pronoun.

He does *good* work.

The italicized word is an adjective because it modifies the noun *work*.

Adjectives modify nouns by answering these questions:
What kind? a *small* dog, an *old* house
How many? *several* days, *six* children
How much? *some* candy, *little* fun
Whose? *Bill's* bike, *her* dress

Kinds of adjectives. Most adjectives are thought of as *descriptive*; they describe nouns or pronouns.

Descriptive adjectives can be *common* (relating to a class of things: a *pretty* girl, a *dull* movie, a *sweet* fruit) or *proper* (relating to one particular member of a class: *American* music, *English* history, *French* horn).

Indefinite adjectives, *possessive* adjectives, and some *relative* adjectives may be used as pronouns: *each, every, neither, both, some, any.*

every day, each person, some books

Relative adjectives may also be used as relative pronouns: *who, which, that.*

that store

Sometimes the adjectives *who, what, which,* and *whose* are used as interrogative pronouns.

What did you say?

Numerical adjectives are either cardinal numbers (*one* bird, *two* birds, *three* birds) or ordinal numbers (*first* man, *second* man, *third* man).

Forms of adjectives. Adjectives have different forms to express degrees of comparison. The simple form of the adjective is called the *positive*.

John is a *great* runner.

When two objects are compared, the adjective referring to them is said to be *comparative*.

John is a *brighter* student than Dick.

To form the comparative, add *er* to the positive; or simply *r* if the adjective already ends in *e*.

When a comparison of more than two is made, the adjective is called *superlative*.

Sandra is the *greatest* runner on the team.

The superlative form of the adjective is usually formed by adding *est*, or *st* if the adjective ends in *e*.

Positive	Comparative	Superlative
rough	rougher	roughest
clean	cleaner	cleanest
wise	wiser	wisest

An adjective ending in *y* changes *y* to *i* and adds *er* to form the comparative; the superlative of such an adjective is formed by changing *y* to *i* and adding *est*.

happy, happier, happiest
busy, busier, busiest

PRACTICE. Write the required forms of these adjectives in the blanks at right.

Positive	Comparative	Superlative
1. early	_____	_____
2. low	_____	_____
3. fine	_____	_____
4. pretty	_____	_____

All adjectives that consist of three or more syllables form the comparative with the aid of the word *more*; to express the superlative, *most* is used. Some adjectives of only two syllables are also formed this way.

Positive	Comparative	Superlative
beautiful	more beautiful	most beautiful
wonder-ful	more wonder-ful	most wonder-ful
careful	more careful	most careful
formal	more formal	most formal

There are some irregular adjectives which should be learned.

Positive	Comparative	Superlative
ill (bad)	worse	worst
far	farther	farthest
good (well)	better	best
little	less	least
many (much)	more	most

An adjective derived from a proper noun begins with a capital, just like the proper noun itself.

Rome, Roman; America, American; Mexico, Mexican; England, English

Predicate adjectives. When an adjective is the predicate of the sentence and acts as a modifier of the subject, the adjective is called a *predicate adjective.* It follows a form of the verb *to be* (*am, is, was, were, has been,* etc.), or it follows a linking verb.

The secretary is *tired*.
Jane was *sleepy*.
I feel *great*.

Notice that the predicate adjective *completes* the meaning of the verb and is therefore called a *complement.* An adjective after a linking verb shows some quality or condition of the subject. Some linking verbs are based on the senses: *see, feel, taste, smell, look, sound.* Other examples of linking verbs are *become, seem, appear, grow,* and *prove.*

It might prove *disastrous*.

Adjective clauses. Sometimes an entire subordinate clause can act as an adjective and modify a noun or pronoun in the main or independent clause.

I knew a boy *whose hobby was catching butterflies*.
The boy was proud of the ball *that he caught*.

The adjective clause is discussed further in other parts of this book.

Position of Adjectives. The adjective often precedes the noun it modifies. Sometimes, for special emphasis or effect, the adjective comes after the noun.

The hero, *proud* and *cocky*, paraded in style.

The use of the two adjectives in the sentence above creates an *adjective phrase.*

PRACTICE. Underline the proper form of the adjectives in parentheses.

1. He is (more, most) studious than his brother.

2. The woman had to go a (farther, fartherer) distance than her daughter to get to the store.

3. The student is sometimes (intelligenter, more intelligent).

4. That was the (most beautiful, beautifullest) music I had ever heard.

5. Of all the streets in the city, this one is the (most narrower, narrowest).

6. His work as an electrician was the (most dangerous, dangerousest) job he ever had.

7. There are many people of (mexican, Mexican) heritage in the Southwest.

8. Of all his subjects, he was (less, least) interested in math.

UNIT 14 ▽ APPLICATION
Adjectives

Fill in the missing words in these sentences. When necessary, the positive form of the adjective is supplied in parentheses.

For
Scoring

1. The comparative of the adjective *liberal* is _____ . _____

2. The superlative of *liberal* is _____ . _____

3. The comparative of the adjective *merry* is _____ . _____

4. John is _____ than Greg. (studious) _____

5. This company pays _____ wages than that one across the street. (high) _____

6. An adjective that ends in *y* forms its comparative by changing _____ to _____ and adding _____ . _____

7. He gets concerned when someone does _____ work than he. (good) _____

8. Helen Yosterling is the _____ of all the typists in the office. (accurate) _____

9. Her Aunt Mary is the _____ of her mother's six sisters. (beautiful) _____

10. Both cartons were received in bad condition; I hardly know which was the _____ . (bad) _____

11. Of the two plans proposed, I think the one that Mr. Jones has outlined is the _____ . (good) _____

12. His cold is much _____ this morning. (bad) _____

13. That appalling crime was the _____ in the history of the state. (bad) _____

14. I have looked up the distances to both Parkersburg and Wheeling, and I find

   that Wheeling is the _____ . (far) _____

15. If you want the _____ of these two pupils to do the work,

   you should choose William. (careful) _____

Underline the adjective clause *once* and the predicate adjective *twice* in each of these sentences. Some sentences have both.

16. The teacher whose class won first prize was elated at the news. _____

17. Marble feels cold to the touch. _____

18. The vegetables that we picked were spoiled when we got home. _____

19. The children were exhausted. _____

20. The actress who won the Oscar last year was surprised to win again this

   year. _____

Underline the correct form in parentheses to complete each of these sentences.

21. Some forms of advertising are (personaler, more personal) than others. _____

22. Although they may all claim to be objective, successful ads are (subtler,

   more subtle) psychologically. _____

23. To influence buying behavior through advertising is an attempt to make the

   buyers feel (good, more better) about what they buy. _____

24. In many ads, the drawings, layouts, and decorative designs are (appealinger,

   more appealing) than in others. _____

25. Writers who compose jingles for advertising agencies are the (sharpest,

   sharper) of all copywriters. _____

UNIT 15
The Articles ▽
Demonstrative Pronouns and Adjectives

The articles. The words *the*, *a*, and *an* are called articles. Because they always modify nouns, articles do the work of adjectives. *The* is used to point out a *definite* person or thing; therefore, it is called a *definite article*. *A* and *an*, on the other hand, are used when no *particular* person or thing is meant; therefore, they are called *indefinite* articles.

the book, the house (definite article)
a book, a house (indefinite article)

A and *an* are used only with a singular noun; *the* may be used with singular or plural nouns.

The distinction between *a* and *an* is very simple. Use *a* before all words that begin with a *consonant* sound. Use *an* before all words that begin with a vowel sound: *a*, *e*, *i*, *o*, or *u*. *Y* is also a vowel when pronounced as *i*, but this seldom happens at the beginning of a word. *Y* is a consonant when it begins a word such as *yard*, *year*, *yacht*, or *yoke*.

Words like *uniform* and *university* do not begin with a sounded vowel. The first sound is really consonant *y*, and therefore, *a* is used before such words.

a uniform, a university

BUT an uninformed person;
an uninteresting book

The *h* in *hour* and *heir* is silent.

an hour, an heir

But *a* is used before words beginning with a sounded *h*.

a hair, a history, a human

Repeat the article before connected adjectives that modify different nouns, one of which may be understood and not expressed.

The red and the green carpet are both in storage.

When the adjectives refer to the same noun, only one article is needed.

The red and green carpet is in storage.

PRACTICE. Underline the correct articles in these sentences.

1. I arrived about (the, a, an) hour ago.

2. Mr. Johnson was (the, a, an) umpire who made that decision.

3. She gave (a, an) special economics text to the new student.

4. We have been offered (the, a, an) hundred dollars for that desk.

5. They wanted to have (the, a, an) agreement of some kind before noon.

6. What (the, a, an) uninteresting play that is!

7. Whenever such (the, a, an) emergency arises, call the operator.

8. We did have (the, a, an) understanding with Mr. Gutowski, but it was not in (the, a, an) form of a contract.

9. There will be (the, a, an) extra charge for these chairs, but we can't tell you (the, a, an) amount right now.

Demonstrative pronouns and adjectives. The words *this* (and *these*) and *that* (and *those*) are demonstrative pronouns and demonstrative adjectives.

SINGULAR	PLURAL
this	**these**
that	**those**

This and *these* indicate or demonstrate nearer objects; *that* and *those* refer to more distant objects.

This is the book you need for that class.

That book is the one we used last year.

In these sentences, *that* is a demonstrative adjective.

These demonstrative words are often used to describe nouns or pronouns and are, therefore, also adjectives.

This book is mine. That one is his.

These cars are new. Those cars are old.

This carries with it the idea that the object is "here," and *that* suggests that the object is "there." Avoid the use of *this here* and *that there*, which are not standard forms of English.

Mistakes are often made when *this* and *that* are used to modify the nouns *kind* and *sort*.

We have never used that kind of pencil.

NOT: We have never used those kind of pencils.

I don't concern myself with this sort of problem.

NOT: I don't concern myself with these sort of problems.

The singular form of both nouns must be kept.

That kind of pencil
This sort of problem

If the plural is used, the plurals must agree throughout.

Those kinds of pencils
These sorts of problems

Remember that *them* cannot be used for *those*. *Them* is never an adjective.

He showed me those pencils.
Not: He showed me them pencils.

PRACTICE. Fill in the blanks with the correct adjectives: **this, that, these,** or **those.**

These objects are nearer.

These objects are more distant.

1. _____ sort of house

2. _____ libraries

3. _____ kind of company

4. _____ analyses

5. _____ stimuli

6. _____ children

7. _____ kinds of sentences

8. _____ sorts of clothes

9. _____ sort of flavor

10. _____ cities

Fill in the blanks with **this, that, these,** or **those.**

11. Are you looking carefully at _____ sentences in front of you?

12. _____ kinds of knives in the shops are always dull.

13. I have often seen _____ kind of machine. (nearer object)

14. We have never had _____ sort of difficulty before. (more distant object)

UNIT 15 ▽ APPLICATION

The Articles ▽
Demonstrative Pronouns and Adjectives

Write the correct choice of the words in parentheses in the blanks at right.

For
Scoring

1. (This, These) kinds of oranges grow in California. _____ _____

2. It seems that (this, these) kind of paper will serve our purpose. _____ _____

3. I don't believe (that, those) data are correct. _____ _____

4. (This, These) tables are sturdier than (that, those) across the room. _____ _____

5. She showed me (them, those) dresses. _____ _____

6. They worked for (a, an) hour longer today than yesterday. _____ _____

7. He was (a, an) uninformed participant. _____ _____

8. We never had such (a, an) emergency as that. _____ _____

9. His father was (a, an) honest man who always worked too hard. _____ _____

10. Did you take the books back to (a, an, the) central library on 24th Street? _____ _____

11. We'll enter into (a, an, the) agreement of some kind with you. _____ _____

12. Here is (a, an, the) sole invoice you asked me to send you. _____ _____

13. She described (this, this here) park from pictures she'd seen. _____ _____

14. (That, That there) scene is picturesque. _____ _____

15. (That, Those) data were supplied by our researchers. _____ _____

16. He could not think of (a, an, the) excuse for being late. _____ _____

17. They studied (a, an, the) history of South America in the last unit. _____ _____

18. Who was (a, an, the) one that decided to cut all the funds? _____ _____

19. Although she liked (this, these) kind of bread, she didn't like (that, those) sort of cheese. _____ _____

20. He never did enjoy (that, those) kinds of sports. _____ _____

21. Most people would like to buy a good house in (a, an, the) desirable kind of area. _____ _____

22. (These, those) people who bought houses instead of renting have been able to get ahead financially. _____ _____

23. (This, This here) fact was due to inflation, which caused the value of houses to increase greatly. _____ _____

24. A prospective house buyer should keep these three things in mind about buying a house: it can be a method of forced saving; it can be a long-term investment; and it can be (a, an) income tax shelter. _____ _____

25. It is hard to beat (those kinds, this kind) of economic benefits. _____ _____

UNIT 16
Adverbs

Kinds of adverbs ▽
Conjunctive adverbs ▽
The adverb clause

Adverbs. An adverb is a word that is used to modify or qualify a verb, an adjective, or another adverb.

He learns *quickly*.
He is an *extraordinarily* happy child.
That study was *completely* wrong.

Most adverbs are formed by adding *ly* to an adjective.

clear, clearly; former, formerly

An adjective that ends in *y* changes *y* to *i* and adds *ly* to form the verb.

happy, happily; ordinary, ordinarily

Many adjectives ending in *e* are made into adverbs by dropping the *e* and adding *y* or *ly*.

true, truly; forcible, forcibly

Adjectives that end in *al* may usually be made into adverbs by adding *ly*. The adverb, therefore, has two *l's* before the *y* ending.

usual, usually; superficial, superficially

Some adjectives are made into adverbs by adding *ally*.

basic, basically; specific, specifically

Like adjectives, adverbs have comparative degrees—*positive, comparative*, and *superlative*. The positive degree is the regular form of the adverb; the sign of the comparative is *er*; and the sign of the superlative is *est*.

soon, sooner, soonest; late, later, latest

Most adverbs, however, are compared with the help of *more* and *most*.

carefully, more carefully, most carefully

A few adverbs are compared irregularly.

well, better, best; far, farther, farthest; far, further, furthest

Kinds of adverbs. Adverbs are classified according to purpose.

Adverbs of time tell *when* or *how often* an action will take place, e.g., *early, frequently, again, formerly*. They answer the question *when?*

He will come *now*. She will come later.

Adverbs of place tell *where* an action will occur, e.g., *away, outside, forward, upward*.

Although they have been *there*, they are coming *here*.

Adverbs of manner tell *how* or *in what manner* the action is done, e.g., *neatly, sincerely, well, kindly*.

He traveled *slowly* on his bike.

Adverbs of degree tell to what *degree, extent*, or *measure* the action is done: *how much, how little*. Some examples are *quite, merely, rather, very*.

Dewey was *almost* elected president.

Adverbs of affirmation and negation tell whether something is true or false, affirmed or negated, e.g., *yes, no, indeed, doubtless*.

Michele is *not* coming today.

PRACTICE. Underline the adverb in each sentence and write what type it is in the blank at right. *Example:* She dresses <u>neatly</u>. (manner)

1. We shall be very glad to come to your party. _____

2. Your payment is considerably overdue. _____

3. He worked most carefully by himself. _____

4. She came here to rest and relax. _____

Conjunctive adverbs. The *conjunctive adverb* acts as a conjunction, or joining word, and as an adverb. As a conjunction, the word joins two independent clauses. As an adverb, the word modifies the whole dependent clause in which it appears.

He said that *however* the vote went, he would support the team's decision.

He said that he would support the team's decision; *however*, the close vote caused him to demand a recount.

In the first sentence, *however* is used as an adverb to modify the verb *went*. In the second sentence, the word *however* is used as a conjunctive adverb to join the two independent clauses. Some commonly used conjunctive adverbs are *consequently, furthermore, hence, however, moreover, nevertheless, still, then,* and *therefore*.

The adverb clause. Some subordinate clauses do the work of adverbs and are called *adverb clauses*. These adverb clauses are introduced by *subordinate conjunctions: when, wherever, where, everywhere, why, because, since, as, so, that, how, as if, as though, on what condition, if, unless, though,* and *although*.

***Since he was late*, he lost his option to bid on the farm.**

The adverb clause modifies the verb *lost* by explaining *why*. The whole clause acts as a single part of speech, the adverb.

Recognizing adverbs. You can determine whether a word is an adjective or an adverb by its use in the sentence. If the word modifies a noun or follows a condition verb, it is an adjective. If the word modifies a verb, adjective, or adverb, that word must be an adverb.

The job was *hard*.

Hard is an adjective here because it follows a form of the verb *be*, which is a condition verb.

She worked *hard* to do the job well.

Hard is an adverb here because it modifies the verb *worked*.

Remember that the word *good* is an adjective only. The corresponding adverb is *well*. They may not be used interchangeably.

She was *good* at sports.
She also did *well* in academics.

PRACTICE. The italicized words in these sentences are either **adjectives** or **adverbs**. Write your choice in the blanks at right.

1. The baby smelled *good*. _____

2. She did *well* on the exam. _____

3. He tried *hard* at everything. _____

4. The precious stone was *hard*. _____

5. They felt *sad* about losing the contest. _____

   In each of these sentences, underline the adverb clause.

6. He looked forward to college partly because he had never lived away from home.

7. Unless her grades improve quickly, she may fail the course.

8. We try to learn something about the native people wherever we travel.

9. Although mortgages are difficult to obtain, we plan to buy a house.

10. We'll all go to Hawaii if you can spare the time.

UNIT 16 ▽ APPLICATION

Adverbs

Write the correct choice of the words in parentheses in the blanks at right for each of these sentences.

For
Scoring

1. If you feel (bad, badly), it is probable that you will do your

   work poorly.   _____ ____

2. She works (efficientlier, more efficiently) after an hour's

   rest.   _____ ____

3. They felt (good, well) about the team effort.   _____ ____

4. Everything he said is (strictally, strictly) confidential.   _____ ____

5. The children (accidently, accidentally) let the dog out of

   the yard.   _____ ____

6. She did such a splendid job that she was commended for

   doing (good, well).   _____ ____

7. They were told to be prepared to move as (quick, quickly)

   as possible.   _____ ____

8. You will need a (considerable, considerably) larger force

   of men.   _____ ____

9. Because the work was (easy, easily), it was finished in

   time.   _____ ____

10. He did the job (satisfactory, satisfactorily).   _____ ____

11. "Let's move very (quick, quickly)," she shouted.   _____ ____

12. We felt (bad, badly) that there were no opportunities for

    advancement.   _____ ____

13. Our intention to raise a million dollars to build a new

    indoor soccer facility is (perfect, perfectly) clear.   _____ ____

14. These tasks can be performed (easy, easily).   _____ ____

15. That illustration in the old family Bible looks (good, well). _____ _____

Identify the adverb clauses below by underlining each of them.

16. Because it was raining, our game against Muhlenberg High

    was canceled. _____

17. Whenever it is rescheduled, I promise to take you. _____

18. They plan to go to the World Series, whenever it is played. _____

19. Since Morris is such an avid baseball fan, I plan to treat

    him to the first home game. _____

20. When his team lost the pennant last year, he wept as

    though it were a personal loss. _____

Identify the italicized adverbs below as **CA** for conjunctive adverbs, **ADV** for adverbs only, or **SC** for subordinate conjunctions. Write your choices in the blanks at right.

21. You failed the test; *consequently*, you must take it again. _____ _____

22. *However* I am feeling tomorrow, I shall cut the grass and

    wash the car. _____ _____

23. Do your personal chores; *then* you may play tennis with

    your friends. _____ _____

24. *Unless* you are finished by four, you may not go with me to

    the circus. _____ _____

25. You know the rules; *therefore*, you are expected to abide

    by them. _____ _____

UNITS 14–16 ▽ RECAP

Adjectives ▽ The Articles ▽ Demonstrative Pronouns and Adjectives ▽ Adverbs

Here are the highlights of the guides relating to adjectives, the articles, demonstrative pronouns and adjectives, and adverbs.

Adjectives as modifiers. Most adjectives modify nouns or pronouns by describing them.

Descriptive adjectives. There are two kinds: common and proper.

Other types of adjectives. Other types of adjectives are indefinite, possessive, relative, numerical, and demonstrative.

Predicate adjective. The predicate adjective follows forms of the verb *be* or linking verbs.

Adjective clause. The whole adjective clause acts as an adjective to modify a noun in the main or independent clause.

Degrees. Adjectives have three degrees: positive, comparative, and superlative.

Articles. The articles *the*, *a*, and *an* always do the work of adjectives by modifying nouns. *The* is called a *definite* article; *a* and *an* are *indefinite* articles. *A* is used before all words that begin with a consonant sound; *an* is used before vowel sounds.

Demonstrative pronouns. *This*, *that*, *these*, and *those* are demonstrative adjectives or pronouns. They must agree in number with the nouns they modify.

Adverbs as modifiers. An adverb modifies a verb, an adjective, or another adverb. Sometimes an adverb can modify a whole sentence.

Classes of adverbs. Adverbs are classified according to kinds: manner, degree, time, place, affirmation, and negation.

Degrees of adverbs. Like adjectives, adverbs have three forms or degrees: positive, comparative, and superlative. Sometimes adverbs and adjectives can only be distinguished by the work they perform in a specific sentence.

Conjunctive adverbs. These adverbs act as both joining words and as adverbs.

Adverb clauses. Subordinate clauses introduced by subordinate conjunctions are called adverb clauses.

Read the example sentences below to determine which correctly illustrates the guide indicated. Write the letter of the correct choice in the blank at the right.

For
Scoring

1. Descriptive adjective.
   a. The *sour* lemon added flavor to the drink.
   b. He was prejudiced in favor of *that* project.

_____ _____

2. Indefinite adjective.
   a. She rode more than 50 miles on *her* bike.
   b. The company provided benefits to *each* worker. _____ _____

3. Superlative degree of adjective.
   a. I have never seen a *more happy* baby than Jason.
   b. Jason is the *happiest* baby I have ever seen. _____ _____

4. Predicate adjective.
   a. Miss Brown is an *efficient* secretary.
   b. Miss Brown is *efficient*. _____ _____

5. Adjective clause.
   a. She is the girl *who won the prize.*
   b. She likes to dance *to rock music.* _____ _____

6. Indefinite article.
   a. He is *the* boy that delivers papers.
   b. He is *an* energetic boy. _____ _____

7. Correct use of *this* and *that.*
   a. This car is new; that car is old.
   b. This here box is full; that there box is empty. _____ _____

8. Correct use of *these* and *those.*
   a. These kind of pencils are useful.
   b. Those sorts of problems are ordinary. _____ _____

9. Adverb of manner.
   a. The students studied *intensely* for the exam.
   b. The voice student practiced her scales *frequently.* _____ _____

10. Adverb in comparative degree.
    a. His younger brother worked more willingly than he.
    b. His younger brother was more willing to work than he. _____ _____

In the following sentences, write the correct form of the words in parentheses in the blanks at right.

11. She showed me (them, those) pictures. _____ _____

12. There will be (a, an, the) extra film shown tomorrow. _____ _____

13. Bill felt (bad, badly) about causing their auto accident. _____ _____

14. All the students did (good, well) on the test today. _____ _____

15. That store is the (busier, busiest) in the shopping mall. _____ _____

16. The teacher said the books were (ours, our's) to keep. _____ _____

17. Because the little girl seemed so (sad, sadly), her mother bought her a toy. _____ _____

18. The attendants parked the cars (careless, carelessly). _____ _____

19. The judges said that the young man danced the (most graceful, most gracefully) of all the ballet troupe. _____ _____

20. These (kind, kinds) of products sell very quickly. _____ _____

UNIT 17
Prepositions ▽
Conjunctions ▽
Interjections

Prepositions. A *preposition* is a word that shows the relation between a noun or pronoun and another word in the sentence.

The water flowed *over* the dam.

Here are some commonly used prepositions:

about	before	except	through
above	behind	for	to
across	below	from	under
against	beside	in	underneath
along	between	into	upon
among	by	of	with
around	down	on	within
at	during	over	without

The word related to the rest of the sentence by means of the preposition is called the object of the preposition. If the object is a pronoun, that pronoun must be in the objective case— *me, her, him, them, us.*

Joan invited all the girls except *her*.

Sometimes the object of the preposition consists of two pronouns joined by *and, or,* or *nor.*

The second pronoun must also be in the objective case.

The argument was between *him and me*.

The preposition *between* is always used when talking about two persons or two objects. *Among* must be used when talking about three or more persons or things.

The decision was made *among* us four.

Certain prepositions are always used to show the relation between nouns or pronouns and certain verbs or adjectives.

accompanied *by* persons or animals;
accompanied *with* objects (such as a letter);
angry *at* a thing;
angry *with* a person;
comply *with* (a request);
differ *with* in thought;
differ *from* in appearance;
different *from* (never different *to* or different *than*)

The word *than* is *not* a preposition. When using constructions with the words *differ* and *differently*, the word *than* is never used.

This coat is different from the one I wore yesterday.

She expressed her idea differently from the way you have repeated it.

The shapes of these boxes differ from the shapes of the others.

PRACTICE. Underline the prepositions in the following sentences.

1. He worried so much about the future that he could not get through the day.

2. Although her mother said the cat was on the roof, Tab was under the porch.

3. During the summer, he liked to spend time with his friends.

4. The assistant in the office brought the mail for all the managers.

    Underline the correct word in the parentheses for each sentence.

5. Give it to (she, her), for her duties are no different (than, from) any of the others in the office.

6. I'd like to differ (with, from) your idea for (her, she) in the sales meeting.

7. (He and I, Him and me) shared the responsibility (between, among) us.

Conjunctions. A *conjunction*, like a preposition, is a word that is used to connect words or groups of words. There are two main kinds of conjunctions: *coordinating* and *subordinating*.

Coordinating conjunctions, such as *and, but, or, nor, for, yet,* and *so,* are used to join words, phrases, or clauses of *equal rank.*

Mary *and* Jane

on the bureau *or* in the drawer

She didn't invite me, *and* I didn't go.

Subordinating conjunctions, such as *although, as, because, if, since, than, though, unless, until,* and *while,* are used to subordinate a clause of lesser rank to an independent or main clause and to connect the lesser clause to the main clause.

He was told not to play *until* the signal was given.

She went to bed early *because* she was tired.

Correlative conjunctions are a few special conjunctions that are always used in pairs: *either . . . or; neither . . . nor; both . . . and; not only . . . but.*

Either Mary *or* Alice is leading the team.

Neither Ben *nor* Harry brought the cake.

The conjunction *than* is often used to connect a single word after words that precede it. If the word that follows is a pronoun, it must be in the nominative case.

He is a better swimmer than I (am).

The conjunction *as* is often repeated to make a comparison.

He is *as* busy *as* I (am).

If the thought is negative, however, *so . . . as* must be used rather than *as . . . as.*

He is not *so* busy *as* I.

The word *like* is not used as a conjunction. Instead, use *as* or *as if.*

Do *as* I say, not *as* I do.
He talks *as if* he wants to do the job.

Interjections. The *interjection* is a word that is used to express emotion or strong feeling. It is followed by an exclamation mark (!). It functions as an independent element, without grammatical relation to other parts of the sentence. Some common interjections are: *Ah!, Oh!, Alas!, Indeed!, Help!, Hurrah!, So!, Welcome!,* and *Well!*

Oh! You scared me to death!

PRACTICE. Underline the conjunctions in the following sentences. Identify your choices as **C** for coordinate, **S** for subordinate, or **CC** for correlative. Write your selections in the blanks at right.

1. Neither thunder nor lightning could frighten her dog.　　　　_____

2. She tried to buy a dress, but they didn't have her size.　　　　_____

3. Although it was cloudy, it did not rain.　　　　_____

4. Since his logic was faulty, he failed lamentably.　　　　_____

5. Both Richard and Henry won athletic scholarships.　　　　_____

Underline the correct words in the parentheses for each sentence.

6. Neither George (or, nor) Paul (is, are) here at present.

7. Both energy (and, or) resourcefulness (is, are) required for this task.

8. Al is not (so, as) handsome as (he, him).

9. Elizabeth is better than (he, him) at nailing up the panels.

UNIT 17 ▽ APPLICATION

Prepositions ▽ Conjunctions ▽ Interjections

Select the correct word from the parentheses and write it in the blank at right.

For
Scoring

1. The four cheerleaders divided the cheers (between, among) them.   _____ _____

2. On his trip to Hawaii, Mr. Anderson was accompanied (by, with) several friends.   _____ _____

3. Between you and (I, me), I don't think he enjoyed him and her.   _____ _____

4. I am certain that nothing will come between him and (she, her).   _____ _____

5. There was no one to be seen in the administrator's office except (he, him).   _____ _____

6. If you and (me, I) do the review carefully, I don't think we can go wrong.   _____ _____

7. Maxwell McKinnon is very different (than, from) his younger sister.   _____ _____

8. Our next report will be accompanied (by, with) all the relevant details.   _____ _____

9. We shall write the specifications so that they will conform (to, with) your plan.   _____ _____

10. I cannot comply (with, to) your rule for the signing of the contract.   _____ _____

11. He was so angry (with, at) the dog that he became angry with me.   _____ _____

12. If you study (as, so) hard as Ingrid, you may graduate
    with honors. _____ _____

13. Marguerite's sister was not (so, as) studious as Pene-
    lope. _____ _____

14. Neither Mr. Henry (or, nor) Ms. Gutierrez will represent
    the rowing team. _____ _____

15. He and I have never been (as, so) busy as we are now. _____ _____

16. I have seldom met a person who is as sympathetic (as,
    like) Robin McMasters. _____ _____

17. A year's supply of bats and balls was given to (he, him). _____ _____

18. Gloria can play the piano and the harpsichord as well as
    (I, me). _____ _____

19. Simon talks (like, as if) he wants to do the schedule
    himself. _____ _____

20. Sebastian Nikilovich insists that he can hit the ball better
    than (I, me). _____ _____

21. Ancient man did not have (so, as) many pressures on him
    as the people of today have. _____ _____

22. Neither the environmental conditions (or, nor) the norms
    for daily living are any longer ideal. _____ _____

23. Alas! We have to wonder whether technological progress
    is (as, so) wonderful as its supporters contend. _____ _____

24. Although evolution has made him different (than, from)
    his ancient cousins, modern man has the same impera-
    tive to adapt to the wear and tear of daily life as they did. _____ _____

25. In his distress, modern man may talk (like, as though) he
    would wish to eliminate all stress, but it is still necessary
    for him to adapt to stress in order to survive. _____ _____

UNIT 18
Verbals

Infinitives ▽ Participles ▽ Gerunds

Verbals are words derived from verbs and used as other parts of speech, such as nouns, adjectives, and adverbs.

Infinitives. The infinitive is the first of the principal parts of the verb. The infinitive comes from the Latin word *infinitus*, which means *without limitations*. It is so called because it is a verb form that is not limited in person and number.

The infinitive is used as a *noun*, as an *adjective*, or as an *adverb*. It is commonly introduced by the word "to," which is called the *sign* of the infinitive.

to sing
to dance
to work
to play

However, the sign "to" may be omitted in the use of the infinitive, especially after the auxiliary verbs *may, can, will, shall, must*, and a few other selected verbs, such as *make, see, hear, feel*.

We saw the truck *collide* with the car.

The officer saw him *walk away* from the scene of the accident.

The infinitive has two tenses: the *present* and the *perfect*.

to see	**to have seen**
to give	**to have given**
to go	**to have gone**

The infinitive *to be* calls for special attention. When a pronoun is used to complete the meaning of *to be*, that pronoun must be in the *nominative case*.

He believes the best actress *to be she*.

I should like *to be he*.

It was mistakenly thought *to be I*.

If, however, the infinitive *to be* has a subject, that subject must be in the objective case.

I believe *them* to be the thieves.

In this case, a pronoun that completes the meaning of *to be* must be in the objective case.

They believed *him* to be *me*.

Remember to use the same case after the infinitive as before it.

Split Infinitive. As a general rule, the infinitive should not be split.

Avoid: *To* properly *mark* the papers, you need *to* closely *examine* them.

Rather: *To mark* the papers properly, you need *to examine* them closely.

Sentences that begin with an infinitive phrase should be worded in such a way that the infinitive logically modifies the subject of the sentence.

To verify the quotation, Mr. Howard consulted this book.

NOT: To verify the quotation, this book was consulted by Mr. Howard.

Uses of the Infinitive. It is most commonly used as a noun.

To forgive is divine.

Here it is used as an adjective:

The urge *to flee* can be healthy in dangerous situations.

In this example, it is used as an adverb:

I looked *to see* if it had started snowing.

Participles. A *participle* shares the nature of a verb and an adjective, and is often called a *verbal adjective*. It is always a modifier.

Smiling, Alice accepted the prize.

However, it can retain one characteristic of verbs: it can take an object.

Anyone *desiring* information should call.

There are three participial forms: present,

past, and perfect. The sign of the present participle is the ending *ing*: e.g., *thinking, hoping, dancing*.

It has been said that dolphins are *talking* animals.

The *dancing* children looked happy.

In these examples, the present participles, *talking* and *dancing*, function as adjectives.

The present participle is used when the time it denotes is the same as the time expressed by the main verb of the sentence. Its form is discussed below.

Seeing the window broken, the police suspected theft.

The past participle is the third primary part of the verb. The form of the past participle is the same as that of the perfect tense (without *have* or *has*): e.g., *thought, danced, hoped*.

Shaken and frightened, Janet called the police to report the accident.

The perfect participle is formed by writing *having* before the past participle form: e.g., *having thought, having danced, having hoped*.

Having worked all night, he went to bed exhausted.

Study these examples:

PRESENT PARTICIPLE	PAST PARTICIPLE	PERFECT PARTICIPLE
writing	written	having written
knowing	known	having known
choosing	chosen	having chosen
seeing	seen	having seen

Because the participle is a *verbal adjective*, it must modify a noun or pronoun.

Jumping and shouting, the *children* made the table collapse.

A common misconstruction known as the "dangling participle" results if the participle is not specifically related to a noun.

Jumping and shouting, the table collapsed under the children.

Did the table dance and sing, too?

Having stretched out on the sand at noon, the sun shone in his eyes.

Did the sun stretch out on the sand? The participles in these cases are misused, or *dangling modifiers*.

The participle must also be placed next to the noun it modifies. A common misconstruction is the *misplaced modifier*.

She ran into a tree, skiing down the mountain.

Was the tree skiing?

Forming the Present Participle. A verb ending in *e* drops the *e* and adds *ing* to form its present participle.

Prove, proving
Leave, leaving
Behave, behaving
Separate, separating

A verb of one syllable that ends with a single consonant preceded by a single vowel doubles the final consonant before adding *ing*.

Plan, planning
Run, running
Ship, shipping

A verb of two syllables that ends with a sounded consonant immediately preceded by a single vowel *and that is accented on the last syllable* also doubles the final consonant before adding *ing*.

Occur, occurring
Concur, concurring
Refer, referring

A verb ending in *y* simply adds *ing*.

Accompany, accompanying
Specify, specifying
Satisfy, satisfying
Embody, embodying

A few verbs that end in *ie* change *ie* to *y* and add *ing*.

Die, dying
Lie, lying
Tie, tying

Note that a participle, like any other adjective, may be modified by an *adverb*.

Having danced *magnificently*, she made six curtain calls.

PRACTICE. Write the participles of the following verbs in the blanks below.

	Present participle	Past participle	Perfect participle
1. Admit	——————	——————	——————
2. Precede	——————	——————	——————
3. Underlie	——————	——————	——————
4. Prefer	——————	——————	——————
5. Disappoint	——————	——————	——————
6. Happen	——————	——————	——————
7. Accept	——————	——————	——————
8. Arrange	——————	——————	——————
9. Notice	——————	——————	——————
10. Win	——————	——————	——————
11. Transfer	——————	——————	——————
12. Vie	——————	——————	——————
13. Destroy	——————	——————	——————
14. Commit	——————	——————	——————

Choose the correct use of the participle in the following pairs of sentences. Write **a** or **b** in the blank at right.

15. a. Squirming and wriggling, I hooked the worm.

    b. Squirming and wriggling, the worm was hooked. _____

16. a. While scrubbing the floor, she broke a tile.

    b. While scrubbing the floor, a tile broke. _____

17. a. After eating a delicious dinner, the dishes were washed.

    b. After eating a delicious dinner, he washed the dishes. _____

18. a. Acting on Mr. Meyers's instructions, these announcements were

       made.

    b. Acting on Mr. Meyers's instructions, Sam made these announce-

       ments. _____

19. a. Shouting in anger, he restrained the dog.

    b. Shouting in anger, the dog was restrained. _____

Gerunds. As the participle is the verbal adjective, the *gerund* is the *verbal noun*. Like the participle, the gerund is a verb form ending in *ing*. How a word is used determines whether it is a gerund or a participle.

Dancing is fun.

Swimming is his sport.

In the examples above, both *dancing* and *swimming* are used as nouns. They are gerunds.

By contrast, *dancing* and *swimming* are both participles in the following sentences.

My great-uncle, Daniel Glassfelter, has *dancing* eyes.

Her eyes, *swimming* with tears, were sore all day.

A gerund may be used as the object; for instance, as an object of a preposition.

She was jealous of her sister's *singing*.

Or, like a verb, a gerund may take an object.

He enjoys *riding* his *bike*.

A noun or pronoun that modifies a gerund must be in the possessive case.

Because he is not familiar with the roads, we are fearful of *his* getting lost.

A pronoun that is used to complete the meaning of the gerund *being* must be in the nominative case.

No one thought of its being *I*.

We were worried about its being *she* who had the accident.

PRACTICE. Identify the gerunds in the following sentences. Write them in the spaces at the right. Then write **S** if the gerund is used as the subject and **O** if the gerund is used as an object.

1. Singing is an art that must be practiced. _____

2. Her being sick was dreadful to us. _____

3. The boys were more interested in the club's hiking

   than in its rules. _____

4. She was frightened by the horse's rearing. _____

5. Knitting the afghan was a time-consuming chore. _____

6. Walking along the seashore was her favorite way to

   spend the evening at the ocean. _____

7. He disliked both begging and stealing. _____

> In the following sentences, identify the infinitive by writing it in the blank at right. Then write **N** if it is used as a noun; **AJ** if it is used as an adjective; or **ADV** if it is used as an adverb.

8. She said he went to work. _____

9. To swim is healthy fun. _____

10. He has a house to sell. _____

11. Are you ready to begin the test? _____

12. To laugh is human. _____

UNIT 18 ▽ APPLICATION

Verbals

In the following sentences, identify the type of verbal in italics as **P** for participle, **G** for gerund, or **I** for infinitive by writing the letter in the blanks at right.

For
Scoring

1. *Jogging* is a popular activity for men and women of all ages. _____ ____

2. People are recommended to read *to keep* abreast of the news. _____ ____

3. *To please* the customers is the aim of the saleswoman from the typesetting company. _____ ____

4. Sven Langerssen was full of admiration for his brother's *skating*. _____ ____

5. *Hiding* in fear, the boy waited for his father's return. _____ ____

6. All of us were happy about its *being* she who won the prize. _____ ____

7. While *fishing* for trout, the delighted angler caught a bass. _____ ____

8. *Having eaten* simply, she was surprised by the amount of the bill. _____ ____

9. *Concerned* for victory, the team resorted to fouls in the last quarter. _____ ____

10. She was a *dancing* doll. _____ ____

11. *Dancing* was Joyce Strenlau's whole life from morning until night. _____ ____

12. The baby learned *to cry* for its bottle. _____ ____

13. He went forth to win friends and *influence* people. _____ ____

14. No one dreamed of its *being* Sally Snodgrass who stole the silver. _____ ____

15. Jane Anderson used soda *to clean* the car battery last night. _____ ____

16. *To share* is a sign of generosity. _____ ____

17. That boy enjoys *dawdling*. _____ ____

18. *Having finished* his work, the exasperated child turned on the television. _____ ____

19. *Having eaten* hurriedly, Nathan got a bad bout of indigestion. _____ ____

20. *To spell* correctly requires knowledge of some rules. _____ ____

21. The neighborhood grocery store, butcher shop, and tailor shop were once *thriving* businesses. _____ ____

22. Once *established*, small stores are considered a valuable part of a shopping mall. _____ ____

23. Each owner was encouraged *to participate* equally in the free enterprise system. _____ ____

24. These same store owners were often neighborhood leaders, creative in the *spawning* of local organizations as well as local charities. _____ ____

25. A proud way of life ended with the *passing* of the privately owned neighborhood store. _____ ____

UNIT 19
Relative Pronouns and Relative Clauses

Relative Pronouns. A pronoun that shows the *relation* between its antecedent and a subordinate clause is called a *relative pronoun*. There are six relative pronouns. They are *who* (*whom, whose*), *that, which,* and *what*.

Who (whom, whose) refers to a person in the antecedent, either masculine or feminine.

She is the girl *who teaches the scouts*.

Notice that *who* changes form to the objective case (whom) and the possessive case (whose). When the relative pronoun is used as the object of a verb of action or the object of a preposition, the objective form *whom* must be used.

She is the girl *whom I saw teaching the scouts*.

These pronouns—*who* (*whom, whose*), *which, that,* and *what*—perform two tasks simultaneously. They work as *pronouns* and as *connectives,* called relative conjunctions.

The case of a relative pronoun (subjective, objective, or possessive) is determined by the function of the pronoun in the clause it introduces.

Here is an example of the subjective case.

The girl *who is knitting by the fire* is my daughter.

Here is an example of the objective case.

The girl *whom you see by the fire* is my daughter.

Here is an example of the possessive case.

The girl *whose face is to the fire* is my daughter.

Sometimes, an expression such as *I thought* or *he says* comes between the relative pronoun *who* and its verb. *Who* is still the subject, however, and must therefore be in the nominative.

The man *who* I thought would come is not here.

Not: The man *whom* I thought would come is not here.

The main clause is *the man is not here*. The fact that the expression *I thought* occurs between the relative pronoun and its verb does not change the case of the pronoun. *Who* is the subject of the relative clause *who would come*.

I saw the man sitting on the bus.

Man is the object of *I saw*.

The man whom I saw was sitting on the bus.

Whom is the object of *I saw*.

The relative pronoun *that* refers to *animals, things,* or *types of people*. It can be masculine, feminine, or neuter. *Which* refers only to *animals* or *things*. It is always neuter.

When one of the relative pronouns is used to introduce a relative clause, you must determine whether the predicate in the relative clause is singular or plural. To arrive at the correct conclusion, determine the word that is the antecedent of the relative pronoun. If it is singular, the predicate in the relative clause must be singular. If the antecedent is plural, however, the predicate in the relative clause must be plural.

English is one of the subjects that *are* required.

NOT: English is one of the subjects that *is* required.

The plural noun *subjects* is the antecedent of the relative pronoun *that*.

Mr. Black is the only one of our representatives who *has reached* the quota.

NOT: Mr. Black is the only one of our representatives who *have reached* the quota.

The antecedent of the relative pronoun *who* is *one*.

PRACTICE. Complete the blanks with the correct form of the relative pronoun: **who, whom,** or **whose.**

1. For _____ is this shipment intended?

2. Timothy Maxted is one of those people _____ it appears are always in a hurry.

3. A man _____ word can be trusted is a delight to know in these troubled times.

4. He is the person _____ I felt should have taken the initiative following the mayor's announcement.

5. Is she the magnificently dressed woman _____ I saw on Market Street?

6. They are the boys _____ were fined for trampling the flowers.

7. She is the one _____ I asked to come.

8. Louise is the dancer _____ choreography is the most original we have ever experienced.

Underline the correct word in the parentheses for each of these sentences.

9. Cynthia Bernardi is the person (which, who) made the decision not to attend the meeting.

10. They removed the animal (who, that) caught its foot in a trap three days ago.

11. The girl (which, whom) you see is the one I recommended for the buyer training program.

12. Stan Woodbridge was the only one of the boys who (were, was) honored at the athletics meeting.

13. Sarah Schwarzenburg is one of those girls who (is, are) always sure of themselves.

14. That is the boy (which, whom) I dislike.

15. He is one of the boys who (is, are) forever late.

16. She is the only one of the sales assistants who (is, are) polite.

Relative clauses. When relative pronouns are thought of as the links between the dependent or *subordinate* clause and the independent or *main* clause, they are known as *relative conjunctions*.

Tom is a boy *who* brags about all his accomplishments.

In this sentence, *Tom is a boy* is the independent clause, *who brags about all his accomplishments* is the dependent clause, and *who* is the relative conjunction.

Clauses introduced by relative conjunctions (or relative pronouns) usually work as adjectives that modify the antecedent of the pronoun. Notice in the example above that the adjective clause introduced by the relative pronoun *who brags about all his accomplishments* modifies the antecedent *boy*. *Who*, therefore, works as an adjective. The word *who* acts as a subject of the verb *brags* and of the whole dependent clause *who brags about all his accomplishments*. The pronoun *who* also introduces its own clause and joins it to the independent clause *Tom is a boy*.

Since the pronoun clause describes the antecedent *boy*, the whole clause works as an adjective. The sentence could read another way, using the adjective *proud* instead of the adjectival clause *who brags about all his accomplishments*.

Tom is a *proud* boy.

Relative clauses are of two kinds, according to the work they do in the sentence: either an *adjective* or *noun clause*. The relative pronoun *what* introduces a subordinate clause used as a noun, i.e., a noun that is the object of the verb.

Examine the story to discover *what the theme is*.

What the theme is acts as the noun *object* of the verb *discover*. *What* is always neuter and can function as a subject or object in the sentence.

What *I think* is my business.

What I think is the noun subject.

Noun clauses can be used in the same way that nouns are used.

Here is a noun clause used as a subject.

Whatever you decide is all right with the rest of us.

Here is a noun clause used as a direct object.

The traffic signal indicates *that we can go*.

John Greenaway greeted *whomever came to the front door*.

Here is a noun clause used as an object of a preposition.

She was not informed about *what was important*.

When an entire clause is the object of the preposition, it is sometimes necessary to use a nominative rather than an objective pronoun, because the pronoun is also the subject of the relative clause in addition to being the object of the preposition.

I bought snacks and drinks for *whoever is here*.

The way to identify a noun clause is by its use in the sentence. Note that the word *that* is sometimes omitted in a noun clause.

You know (that) I'm sorry. I think (that) you are right.

What, who, whom, and *which* are often interrogative pronouns. They are distinguished from relative pronouns by their function in a particular sentence.

Who are the scholarship winners from our school?

What will the country do to improve the economic situation?

The compound relative pronouns commonly used are *whoever, whichever,* and *whatever*. (*Whosoever, whichsoever,* and *whatsoever* are disappearing from use.)

Whatever you decide will be respected by us.

Whoever left the light on is wasting electricity.

According to structure, there are also two kinds of relative clauses: *restrictive* and *nonre-*

strictive. A *restrictive relative clause* is one that restricts the meaning of the word it modifies so that the omission of the restrictive clause would make the meaning of the sentence obscure or deprive it of meaning.

A secretary who has mastered English is on the way to success.

The main clause is *A secretary is on the way to success*. The omission of the restrictive clause *who has mastered English* would destroy the essential meaning of the sentence.

On the other hand, a *nonrestrictive relative clause* is one which simply supplies additional information to the sentence. Such a relative clause could readily make another sentence.

Mr. Karski, who is one of our representatives, will conduct the seminar.

Mr. Karski will conduct the seminar. He is one of our representatives.

The choice between *that* and *which* may vary with the function of the clause. Clauses introduced by *that* are usually restrictive. Clauses introduced by *which* are ordinarily nonrestrictive. *Who* clauses must be analyzed to determine whether they are restrictive or nonrestrictive.

Nonrestrictive clauses are set off from the rest of the sentence by commas. Restrictive clauses, however, are so closely tied into the meaning of the sentence that it would be a mistake to set off such a clause by commas.

PRACTICE. Identify the purpose of the italicized relative clauses in these sentences as **ADJ** for adjectives or **N** for nouns. Write your answers in the blanks at right.

1. A person *who is a compulsive worker* often defeats himself. _____

2. *What she thinks* is usually the opposite of *what she says*. _____

3. Despite *what she did*, he gave her a passing grade. _____

4. The book *that was on the desk* was stolen. _____

5. The papers, *which were not important*, were forgotten in the files. _____

> Underline the relative clauses in these sentences and identify them as **RES** for restrictive or **NONRES** for nonrestrictive by writing the correct label in the blanks at right. (All commas have been omitted.)

6. The man who won the contest is going to Bermuda. _____

7. The saleswoman called on the prestigious Excelsior Company which is located two blocks from our office. _____

8. Jobs that pay well are difficult to find. _____

9. The president is a person whom everyone respects. _____

10. The unnecessary paperwork was locked in old files which were dusty and neglected. _____

UNIT 19 ▽ APPLICATION

Relative Pronouns and Relative Clauses

Fill in the blanks with the correct form of the relative pronoun **who**.

For
Scoring

1. Maria Callas was an opera star _____ was appreciated by millions

   of fans.   _____

2. The lead tenor, _____ parents encouraged him to sing, still lives in

   his native village.   _____

3. He is a man _____ everyone respects.   _____

4. The matter of _____ will represent the firm is being discussed.   _____

5. You are the very man _____ I feel should be interested in this

   invention.   _____

6. A student _____ financial aid is cancelled may have to leave

   college.   _____

7. _____ did the salesman see when he called here?   _____

8. _____ does Mr. Wright believe is the man to lead the project?   _____

9. _____ can we get to do this job properly?   _____

10. The stories vary, depending upon to _____ you talk.   _____

Underline the relative clause in each of these sentences. Then
identify the clauses as restrictive or nonrestrictive by writing **RES**
or **NONRES** in the blanks at right.

11. Don't forget me, whatever you do.   _____ _____

12. The student who studied for many months did very well on

    the final exam.   _____ _____

13. He has what it takes to win.   _____ _____

14. I read an article, which was too long, about the history of

   health fads. _____ _____

15. What he received for Christmas was always a surprise. _____ _____

> Choose the correct word in the parentheses and write it in the
> blank at right.

16. This is one of those movies that (is, are) full of love

   scenes. _____ _____

17. It is the only one that (was, were) appealing to the

   teenagers. _____ _____

18. A child was looking for a marble (whom, that) he had

   lost. _____ _____

19. The man (who, whom) you can trust is not so rare as you

   think. _____ _____

20. She was one of those people (who, whom) always think

   the sky is falling. _____ _____

21. The elementary school teacher was interested in (whoever,

   whomever) could play an instrument. _____ _____

22. She was one of those teachers who (is, are) always

   coming up with new ideas. _____ _____

23. Because she knew there were many young students (who,

   which) had already taken several years of music, she

   thought the school could develop a band. _____ _____

24. It was her principal, (who's, whose) disapproval she did

   not foresee, (whom, who) she had to convince of the

   feasibility of the plan. _____ _____

25. After months of anticipation, the school had a band (who,

   whom, that) presented a fine musical program at the sixth

   grade graduation. _____ _____

UNITS 17–19 ▽ RECAP

Prepositions ▽ Conjunctions ▽ Interjections ▽ Verbals ▽ Relative Pronouns ▽ Relative Clauses

Here are the highlights of the guides relating to prepositions, conjunctions, interjections, verbals (infinitives, participles, and gerunds), relative pronouns, and relative clauses.

Prepositions. A preposition is a word that shows the relationship between a noun and another word in the sentence. The word related to the rest of the sentence by means of the preposition is called the object of the preposition.

Conjunctions. A conjunction is a word that is used to connect words or groups of words.

Coordinating conjunctions. *And*, *but*, *or*, *nor*, *for*, *yet*, *so*, etc., are used to join words or groups of words of equal rank.

Subordinating conjunctions. *Although*, *as*, *because*, *if*, *since*, *than*, *through*, *unless*, *until*, *while*, etc., are used to subordinate and connect a clause of lesser rank to an independent or main clause.

Correlative conjunctions. Special conjunctions that are always used in pairs (*either . . . or*; *neither . . . nor*; *both . . . and*) are correlative conjunctions.

Interjections. An interjection is a word that is used to express emotion or strong feeling. It is followed by an exclamation mark and functions as an independent element in the sentence.

Verbals. Words derived from verbs and used as other parts of speech, such as nouns, adjectives, and adverbs, are verbals.

Infinitives. An infinitive is the first of the principal forms of the verb. It is used as a noun, as an adjective, or as an adverb.

Participles. Participles are forms of the verb that can function as verbal adjectives. There are three participial forms: present, past, and perfect.

Gerunds. The gerund is derived from the verb and functions as a noun. It is called the verbal noun.

Relative pronouns. A relative pronoun (*who*, *whom*, *whose*, *that*, *which*, and *what*) shows the relation between its antecedent and a subordinate clause.

Relative clauses. Dependent clauses introduced by relative pronouns (conjunctions) are called relative clauses. These clauses function as adjectives or as nouns. There are restrictive and nonrestrictive relative clauses.

In the example sentences below, determine which correctly illustrates the guide indicated. Write the letter of the correct sentence in the blank at the right.

For Scoring

1. Use of correct preposition.
   a. The preparations were discussed between the four members.
   b. The preparations were discussed among the four members. _____ _____

2. Correct pronouns as objects of prepositions.
   a. Resolving the argument was a problem between her and him.
   b. Resolving the argument was a problem between she and he. ____ ____

3. Sentence using coordinating conjunction.
   a. He didn't believe me, so I gave up trying to convince him.
   b. Because he didn't believe me, I gave up trying to convince him. ____ ____

4. Sentence using subordinating conjunction.
   a. I will go to the festival if you think it will be fun.
   b. I will go to the festival and I think it will be fun. ____ ____

5. Sentence using correlative conjunctions.
   a. She decided to read Charlotte and Emily Brontë separately or
      to find a book on both authors.
   b. She decided either to read Charlotte and Emily Brontë sepa-
      rately or to find a book on both authors. ____ ____

6. Correct use of interjection.
   a. Oh the temperature will reach 100 degrees today.
   b. Oh! The temperature will reach 100 degrees today. ____ ____

7. Infinitive used as a noun.
   a. To collide with another car was her chief fear in driving.
   b. Cars collide often on the freeway. ____ ____

8. Participle (verbal adjective).
   a. Complaining, the boy refused to cut the lawn.
   b. The boy was punished for complaining and for refusing to cut
      the lawn. ____ ____

9. Gerund (verbal noun).
   a. Complaining is a waste of time.
   b. The complaining child was put to bed. ____ ____

10. Correct use of relative pronouns *who* and *whom*.
    a. The girl who she saw was running for a bus.
    b. The girl whom she saw was running for a bus. ____ ____

11. Relative clause used as a noun.
    a. He believes in bad weather because it brings him good luck.
    b. He believes that the weather influences his luck. ____ ____

In the following sentences, underline the correct form of the
words in parentheses.

12. The six children divided the box of chalk (between, among) them. ____

13. Neither lying (or, nor) cheating can lead to success. ____

14. The application for admission was sent to (they, them) in the office. ____

15. Between (her and him, he and she) there were intense differences. ____

16. They were sick of listening to the sound of (she, her) singing. ____

17. We were worried about its being (she, her) who sang the wrong notes. ____

18. The person (who, whom) I thought would deliver the box has not come. ____

19. All the animals (that, who) live out of cages were selected by Becky. ____

20. The boy (who, whom) you see by the ball field is my son. ____

UNIT 20
Phrases

Noun phrase ▽
Verb phrase ▽
Verbal phrases ▽
Prepositional phrases ▽
Appositive phrase ▽
Absolute phrase ▽
Elliptical phrase

The phrase. A phrase is a group of closely related words that does not have a subject and predicate. Sometimes a phrase may be a subject.

The new class president

Sometimes the phrase may be a verb.

could have been elected.

A phrase is a fragment and may never stand as a sentence. However, when a subject phrase and a verb phrase are combined, they can form a sentence.

The new class president could have been elected.

Any group of two or more related words can constitute a phrase. There are several kinds of phrases: the subject phrase; the verb phrase; verbal phrases (participial phrase, infinitive phrase, and gerund phrase); prepositional phrases (adjective phrase, adverb phrase, and sometimes the noun phrase); the appositive phrase; the absolute phrase; and the elliptical phrase.

Phrases are classified according to *form* by identifying their introductory words as participial, prepositional, etc. They are also classified according to *use* by determining the way the phrase works in the sentence: as a noun, verb, adjective, adverb, etc.

The phrase acts as a single part of speech.

Thus, a *prepositional phrase* may be an adjective or an adverb. A *gerund* phrase would always be a noun. An *infinitive* phrase would be a noun, adjective, or adverb. A *participial phrase* would always be an *adjective*.

Noun phrase. A *noun phrase* contains a noun and its modifiers.

The old, dilapidated farmhouse

Verb phrase. A *verb phrase* contains a main action verb and its auxiliary or helping verbs. It is used to do the work of a single verb.

will give
will have given
will have been given

Verbal phrases. *Verbal phrases* contain any of the three forms derived from the verb—participles, infinitives, and gerunds—plus the words closely related to them.

Participial Phrase. The participial phrase below is an adjective that modifies *boy*. Note that the verbal phrase retains some of the qualities of the verb because it takes a direct object, *the fence*.

***Having painted the fence*, the boy was glad to get his pay.**

The placement of the participial phrase is optional; it may come after the noun or pronoun it limits or modifies, or it may be used as an introductory phrase.

George Washington, *having been an army general*, became president of the United States.

Restrictive and Nonrestrictive Participial Phrases. In both sentences above, the participial phrase is used nonrestrictively, i.e., it is not necessary to the meaning of the sentence. Therefore, it is set off by commas. If the participial phrase is used restrictively, it is *not* set off by commas.

An army general *becoming president of the United States* was to be repeated in history with Dwight Eisenhower.

Infinitive Phrase. The infinitive phrase contains the base form of the verb preceded by *to*, the sign of the infinitive, plus the words that complete the infinitive phrase, which may be objects, complements, or modifiers. Like the infinitive, the infinitive phrase can act as a noun, adjective, or adverb in the sentence.

She doesn't like *to do dishes.*

Here the infinitive phrase is a noun that acts as the object of the sentence.

Few people have money *to burn.*

Here the infinitive phrase modifies the noun *money* and therefore functions as an adjective.

He traveled *to collect antiques.*

Here the infinitive phrase modifies the verb *traveled* and therefore functions as an adverb.

Gerund Phrase. Being verb forms, gerunds can also have objects, complements, and modifiers. The gerund and these words form a gerund phrase, which functions only as a *noun.*

***Eating vegetables* provides healthful nourishment.**

Vegetables is the object of the gerund *eating.* The phrase *eating vegetables* is the subject of the verb *provides.*

PRACTICE. Identify the phrases in italics as **Noun, Verb**, or **Verbal** phrases. If they are verbals, indicate **P** for participial, **I** for infinitive, and **G** for gerund. Also identify the part of speech: **noun, adjective,** or **adverb.** A typical answer in the blank at right might be **Verbal, P, Adj**.

1. *Counting sheep* helps Consuela Petrucco fall asleep. _____

2. Margaret Underwood's new classical record *was warped.* _____

3. By the time he gets home, he *will have walked* three miles. _____

4. *Taking a deep breath*, Sue dived into the freezing water. _____

5. They all stopped *to listen.* _____

6. She has a strong ambition *to win the beauty contest.* _____

7. *The little, old church on the hill* is attended by Richie Sargeant. _____

8. They *have been swimming* all morning. _____

9. *Vacationing in the Cayman Islands*, she overcame her grief. _____

10. *Vacationing in the West Indies* is Matthew Martinovic's idea of luxury. _____

Prepositional phrases. A prepositional phrase is a group of related words consisting of a preposition, the object of the preposition, and the modifiers of the object. The preposition and its object, the noun or pronoun that follows, form the prepositional phrase. The whole prepositional phrase acts as either an adjective or an adverb most of the time. Occasionally, however, it can act as a noun.

Study this prepositional phrase.

over the roof

Over is the preposition, *the* is the adjective, and *roof* is the object of the preposition.

The object of the preposition answers the question *whom, what, which, where, when,* or *how?*

An adjective phrase may be a prepositional phrase used as an adjective.

The boy *with the long legs* runs like a gazelle.

The adjective *longlegged* could be used to modify the noun *boy*.

An adverbial phrase may be a prepositional phrase used as an adverb.

She shouted *with joy*.

The adverb *joyfully* could replace the phrase *with joy* to modify the verb *shouted*.

Prepositional phrases used as adjectives and adverbs are ordinary and numerous in common usage.

We waited *for the bus*.
She walked *in the park*.
They came *during the night*.
The cat *on the fence*
The frog *beside the pond*

We also use the prepositional phrase as a noun. It is more difficult to identify in these instances.

Look at the following noun phrases:

***Before dinner* is no time to eat candy.**

***Under the bed* is the place to hide the money.**

Notice that both examples of the prepositional phrase used as a noun employ a form of the verb *to be*. This is a linking verb, connecting a subject with a predicate complement. Thus, the prepositional phrase used as a noun functions as either *subject*, as in the examples above, or as *predicate complement*, as in this example:

The place to hide the money is *under the bed*.

Remember that predicate complements can also be adjectives or pronouns.

In the example below, the prepositional phrase is an adverb that tells *where* the money *is*. Thus, it follows that all prepositional phrases coming after forms of the verb *be* are *not* necessarily noun phrases.

The money is *in the house*.

Prepositional phrases are modifying phrases and must always refer to the word they modify.

The man in the blue suit gave you the money.

NOT: The man gave you the money in the blue suit.

Appositive phrase. An appositive plus its modifiers forms an appositive phrase. (The *appositive* is a noun or pronoun, sometimes with modifiers, that is placed directly after another noun or pronoun to modify or explain it.) The appositive and the phrase are both set off by commas when they are not essential to the meaning of the sentence.

In the two sentences below, the first is an example of an appositive and the second is an example of an appositive phrase.

Bobby Preston, *an evangelist*, preaches around the world.

Bobby Preston, *the famous American evangelist who preaches around the world*, is a man of unusual energy.

When an appositive or appositive phrase is essential to the meaning of a sentence, it is not set off.

My son Bill is a surgeon. (I have several sons, but *Bill* is the only one who is a surgeon.)

My son, Bill, is a surgeon. (Bill is my only son.)

An appositive phrase can function as an adjective, as in the examples above, or as a noun, as in this gerund phrase.

His best tactic, *outbidding us*, won him the sale.

Absolute phrase. Sometimes a phrase is grammatically independent from the rest of the sentence. Instead of modifying a particular word in a sentence, this absolute phrase modifies the entire sentence.

The bid won, Mr. Nowakowski and the company president went out to dinner.

Participial phrases plus the noun or pronoun introducing them also form absolute phrases.

The boat having sunk, the sailors were rescued by the Coast Guard.

Infinitives may also form an absolute phrase.

To tell the truth, he didn't come.

Absolute phrases are always set off by commas. Because the absolute construction is abstract, it is difficult to use correctly. However, when used properly, it is a very effective means of adding detail to a sentence.

Elliptical phrase. An *ellipsis*, or omission of words, creates a word grouping that is grammatically incomplete; sometimes this elliptical expression is identified as a phrase.

Our college is large, *his small*.

The ellipsis or missing words *college is* creates the elliptical expression *his small*. If the second part of the sentence had read *his college is small*, then, of course, we would have a clause. (Note that we would then need a semicolon, not a comma, to separate the clauses. In fact, the example above could have been punctuated *our college is large; his, small* because commas are sometimes used to indicate an ellipsis.)

As the expression stands, *his small* is an elliptical phrase.

PRACTICE. Identify the italicized phrases as **P. ADJ.** for Prepositional Adjective; **P. ADV.** for Prepositional Adverb; **P. NOUN** for Prepositional Noun; **ELLIP.** for Elliptical Phrase; **APP.** for Appositive; and **ABSOL.** for Absolute. Place your answers in the blanks at right.

1. The English teacher, *a stickler for grammar*, was especially happy when students could distinguish phrases from clauses. _____

2. She read *under the tree*. _____

3. The house *in the woods* is dilapidated. _____

4. *Before lunch* is the time to take your medication. _____

5. *Her favorite drink*, orange juice, is good for her. _____

6. Their book is famous, *ours unknown*. _____

7. *The singer having finished*, the audience applauded. _____

8. *Before breakfast* is her favorite time to exercise. _____

9. He acted with secrecy *because he was an undercover agent*. _____

10. That lady in the pink bonnet *looks very stylish*. _____

11. *The dinner over*, the graduates went to the prom. _____

UNIT 20 ▽ APPLICATION

Phrases

Identify the italicized phrases as **P. ADJ.** for Prepositional Adjective; **P. ADV.** for Prepositional Adverb; **P.P.** for Participial Phrase; **V.P.** for Verb Phrase; **G.P.** for Gerund Phrase; **N.P.** for Noun Phrase; **APP.** for Appositive; **ABSOL.** for Absolute; and **ELLIP.** for Elliptical. Place your answers in the blanks at right.

For Scoring

1. The half-destroyed church *in the next block* is being rebuilt. _____ ____

2. Students *under pressure* occasionally have been given lessons in meditation. _____ ____

3. *Having rowed* across the river, the scouts rested at the campsite. _____ ____

4. The faithful heart always retains permanent memories *of home*. _____ ____

5. *To tell the truth*, she was anxious to hear the music. _____ ____

6. The violent wind *has ripped* through the trees and knocked three of them down. _____ ____

7. He likes to mow the grass *in the morning*. _____ ____

8. *Waiting for better days* may be a frustrating experience. _____ ____

9. Their climate is hot, *ours cold*. _____ ____

10. Babe Ruth, *the famous slugger*, made his home in Baltimore. _____ ____

11. One of the most interesting aspects of advertising is demographics, *the study of people*, used to identify the target audience and then select media that will reach that audience. _____ ____

12. *These audiences* can be identified by age, sex, education, income, religious preferences, location, etc. _____ ____

13. After the audience is identified, *the most effective types of media* for reaching that audience need to be selected. _____ ____

14. Types of media available *to the advertiser* are as follows: television and radio; periodicals; consumer or trade magazines; car cards for taxicabs and buses; circulars; and skywriting.   _____ ____

15. The reason *for demographics* is the need to determine the most efficient expenditure of the advertising dollar.   _____ ____

In the following sentences, choose **a** or **b** as the sentence containing the phrase given and write the correct letter in the blanks at right.

16. Gerund phrase:
    a. Playing tennis is good exercise.
    b. Playing tennis, she turned and sprained her ankle.   _____ ____

17. Infinitive phrase used as adverb:
    a. To work hard is commendable.
    b. He was ready to work hard.   _____ ____

18. Infinitive phrase used as a noun:
    a. To err at times is human.
    b. A tendency to err often can cause problems.   _____ ____

19. Infinitive phrase used as an adjective:
    a. She has a condominium to rent next month.
    b. He wanted to rent the condominium.   _____ ____

20. Prepositional phrase used as an adjective:
    a. The woman slept in the yard.
    b. The cat in the yard caught the bird.   _____ ____

21. Prepositional phrase used as an adverb:
    a. He jogged around the park.
    b. The flowers around the park are blooming.   _____ ____

22. Prepositional phrase used as a noun:
    a. Before summer is the time to plant vegetables.
    b. She went to Europe before summer every year.   _____ ____

23. Absolute phrase:
    a. When the dance ended, the students went to the restaurant.
    b. The dance having ended, the students went to the restaurant.   _____ ____

24. Elliptical phrase:
    a. Our hopes were high, confidence down.
    b. Our hopes were high; our confidence was down.   _____ ____

25. Appositive phrase:
    a. Leontyne Price is the famous opera star who sang the lead in *Aïda.*
    b. Leontyne Price, the famous opera star, sang the lead in *Aïda.*   _____ ____

UNIT 21
Voice and Mood of Verbs

Active and passive voice ▽
Indicative mood ▽
Imperative mood ▽
Subjunctive mood ▽

Active voice. Like tense, *voice* is a characteristic of verbs. You have learned that six tenses are used to show the time of the action denoted by the verb. The forms of the verbs studied earlier in this book have all been in the *active voice*. The distinction that shows whether the subject acts or is acted upon is called *voice*. It makes clear the relationship between the subject and the action of the verb. If the *subject* performs the action, the verb is in the *active voice*.

Kristin *played* the piano.

If the subject receives the action, the verb is in the *passive voice*.

The piano *was played* by Kristin.

In the first sentence, the subject *Kristin* is represented as performing the act of playing. In the second sentence, the subject *piano* is represented as being acted upon (*played*).

The *active* verb *played* takes the object piano; thus, it is a transitive verb. In the passive sentence, *piano* (the object in the first sentence) now becomes the subject of the *passive* verb *was played*.

Because only transitive verbs take an object, only transitive verbs have a passive voice.

Notice that in the second sentence, the past participle of the verb *play* is combined with the past tense of the helping verb *be*. The passive voice of the verb is always formed by the proper tenses of the verb *be*, followed by the perfect participle of the verb.

PRESENT PERFECT

have been	has been

PAST PERFECT

had been

FUTURE PERFECT

shall have been	will have been

When we combine the perfect form of a verb with a form of *be*, that verb is said to be in the *passive*. In order to understand the passive of the verb, the tenses of the verbs must be reviewed in the active and passive voices.

ACTIVE TENSE	PASSIVE TENSE
Present	
he rides	he is ridden
he is riding	he is being ridden
he does ride	
Past	
he rode	he was ridden
he was riding	he was being ridden
he did ride	
Future	
he will ride	he will be ridden
he will be riding	
Present perfect	
he has ridden	he has been ridden
he has been riding	
Past perfect	
he had ridden	he had been ridden
he had been riding	
Future perfect	
he will have ridden	he will have been ridden
he will have been riding	

Let us take the irregular verbs *break* and *bring* in the passive forms of the third person singular.

PRESENT PASSIVE

it is broken	it is brought

PAST PASSIVE

it was broken	it was brought

PERFECT PASSIVE

it has been broken	it has been brought

You must know the perfect forms of verbs in order to write their passive forms correctly. *Regular verbs*, such as *walk*, form their perfect by adding *ed* to the present tense. However, as you remember, the irregular verbs must be studied to learn their perfect forms. (This would be a good time to review Units 7 and 8 on the forms of irregular verbs.)

As a rule, passive construction is considered awkward and weak because it is often unnatural and not emphatic. Although the active voice is generally stronger and more forceful because it is direct, here are occasions for the *legitimate use of the passive*. Use the passive voice when:

—the occasion demands giving specific emphasis to the receiver of the action.

He was awarded the prize.

—the doer of the action must be deemphasized for some reason.

Many inaccurate reports have been made.

—the doer of the action is not important or significant.

The dishes were done earlier this evening.

—the doer of the action is obvious.

The children in the kindergarten were scolded by the teacher.

—the doer of the action is not known.

The bomb was thrown by someone in the crowd.

PRACTICE. Write the correct passive forms of the verbs given in the present passive.

Present passive	Past passive	Perfect passive
1. Time is given.	_____	_____
2. Bread is eaten.	_____	_____
3. Work is done.	_____	_____
4. Book is bought.	_____	_____
5. It is begun.	_____	_____

Convert the following sentences from active to passive voice.

6. Martin gave the answer to Fernando. _____

7. Gerry DeFreitas handled the rudder. _____

8. Bobby Carpenter has lit the lamp. _____

9. The officers arrested two men. _____

10. The bank no longer takes new mortgages. _____

Moods. In addition to tense and voice, verbs also have mood (or mode; from the Latin *modus* meaning manner), which designates the manner in which action, being, or state is expressed. There are four moods: *indicative*, *imperative*, *subjunctive*, and *potential form*.

Indicative mood.

The indicative mood of the verb is used to make statements and to ask questions. This is the most ordinary and most frequently used mood of the verb in English. Thus, it is also the most important.

Jack and Jill went up the hill.
What is the weather forecast?

Imperative mood.

The imperative mood of the verb is used to make demands, give commands, or make requests. This mood of the verb is used only in the *second person* of the *present tense*. The forms for the singular and the plural are identical. The subject *you* is understood and is usually omitted in the imperative voice.

Bring the car back by noon.
Don't shoot. Salute.
Please write often.

Subjunctive mood.

The subjunctive is the most complex mood of the verb. Future time is implied by the subjunctive, which is the mood of *condition, doubt, desire, imagination,* and *statements contrary to fact.*

Here's how to use it to express condition.

If he *were* to come here, he would have more fun.

Here's how to use it to express doubt.

If this *be* our new instructor, then children are our best teachers.

Here's how to use it to express a wish or command.

I wish I *were* on vacation.
I insist that the money *be* returned.

Here's how to use it to express imagination.

If it *were* to rain pennies, we would all be rich.

Here's how to use it to express statements contrary to fact.

He acts as if he *were* the boss.

Verbs in the subjunctive mood have one form different from the corresponding indicative form. The verb *to be*, the main verb used in the subjunctive, is used in two forms.

Be is used for all persons in the present tense.

I be, you be, we be, he be, they be

Were is used for the first and third persons of the past tense.

I were, you were, he were, we were, they were

Here are the present indicative forms.

I am, you are, he is, we are, they are

Here are the past indicative forms.

I was, you were, he was, we were, they were

All the forms of the subjunctive are not used in English as commonly today as they were formerly. However, there are two categories of usage of the subjunctive that are still necessary to proper use of English.

The first is in condition contrary to fact: the use of *if* and *though* clauses.

If she *were* principal, the rules would be changed.

Though he *were* poor, he would still give generously.

However, if the condition is presented not as untrue but only as doubtful or uncertain, the present subjunctive is used.

If it is suggested that she *be* principal, we are in for tighter discipline.

The second is in *that* clauses after verbs of asking, urging, insisting, requesting, ordering, demanding, recommending, etc.

He urged that the amendment *be* passed.

She moved that the meeting *be* adjourned.

It is necessary that they *be* contacted.

Notice this example.

Is it necessary that the cheating student *fail*?

In the indicative, the verb *fail* should end in *s* in the third person. In the subjunctive, the *s* is omitted.

The subjunctive is very much alive in expressions built into the language as idioms.

God *bless* you.
(NOT: God blesses you.)

Far *be* it from me to say. . . .
(NOT: It is far from me to say. . . .)

If *it were* only true!
(NOT: If it *was* only true!)

Potential Form. Special helping verbs called *modal auxiliaries*, such as *may, can, must, might, ought, could, would,* and *should,* are used with verbs to create modal aspects that are sometimes called the *potential form* of the indicative mood or the *potential mood* of the verb.

These modal auxiliaries are important because of their frequent use in standard verb phrases: *might stay; should try; may go.*

The potential form expresses permission, possibility, ability, obligation, and necessity.

These forms may be active or passive.

Jim could pay the bill. (active)
The bill could be paid by Jim. (passive)

PRACTICE. Identify the mood of the verbs in the following sentences as **I** for Indicative, **IMP** for imperative, **S** for subjunctive, and **PF** for potential form. Write your choices in the blanks at right.

1. The company has borne all the expenses of the investigation. _____

2. Read each sentence carefully. _____

3. We ought to be on time. _____

4. I wish there were more salespersons in the northeastern territory. _____

5. Please examine the paper company's merchandise carefully. _____

6. If it were only true that you love me! _____

7. Alicia and Herb have recently been married. _____

8. You would believe in the project. _____

9. Say "hello" to Veronica and Patrick when you walk in the room. _____

10. Tom Florentine must paint his father's fence today. _____

11. How often has George Skouras gone to Cleveland this year? _____

12. Have all the kindergarten children in this class been vaccinated? _____

13. I may come with you tomorrow. _____

UNIT 21 ▽ APPLICATION

Voice and Mood of Verbs

Identify the voices of the verbs in these sentences as **A** for active or **P** for passive. Write your choices in the blanks at right.

For
Scoring

1. She went to college on a scholarship.   _____ _____

2. They were given assignments that took hours to

   complete.   _____ _____

3. Mr. Kenyatta has written a new book.   _____ _____

4. These apartments were recommended by a friend.   _____ _____

5. The friend who recommended the apartments used to live

   in one of them.   _____ _____

6. If we believe that story, we are all fools.   _____ _____

7. It is necessary that he admit he is wrong.   _____ _____

8. We have been given some used furniture to decorate the

   apartment.   _____ _____

9. His scout troop will have been disbanded by the time he

   is twenty.   _____ _____

10. May you be blessed a hundredfold!   _____ _____

In the following sentences, choose the correct form in the parentheses of the verb **be** for the subjunctive voice. Write your answers in the blanks.

11. I wish I _____ your friend. (am, were)   _____

12. They proposed that he _____ graduated. (be, was)   _____

13. She may _____ there tomorrow. (was, be)   _____

14. They demanded that he _____ present. (be, is)   _____

15. I move that the resolution _____ adopted. (is, be)   _____

16. She asked that both students _____ listed on the honor roll. (are, be)

____

17. _____ we to delay our departure, we may have to decide on that now. (Are, Were)

____

18. Would that Mrs. Wright _____ more responsible! (was, were)

____

19. If this law _____ to be passed, equality in the employment market would be enforceable. (were, is)

____

20. Discipline demands that you _____ alert. (be, are)

____

Identify the italicized verbs in the following sentences according to voice by writing **A** for active or **P** for passive and then according to mood by writing **I** for indicative, **IMP** for imperative, **S** for subjunctive, or **PF** for potential form in the blanks at right. A typical answer might be **P - S**.

21. *Use* parliamentary procedure to conduct a meeting in an orderly fashion.

_____ ____

22. If the group or organization *be interested* in strict standards of authority for running their meetings, they are wise to consult a book like *Robert's Rules of Order*.

_____ ____

23. It is necessary that points of order *be raised* if improper procedure occur.

_____ ____

24. When any motion is made, it *must be* approved.

_____ ____

25. "I move the meeting *be adjourned*," she said.

_____ ____

UNIT 22
Kinds of Sentences

Purpose ▽ Structure ▽ Clauses and sentences

Purpose. There are four main purposes of a sentence. It may make a statement; it may ask a direct question; it may express a request or make a demand; and it may indicate strong feeling or emotion.

The grammatical terms or classifications for these four kinds of sentences are:

Declarative: the sentence makes a statement.

Americans are a democratic people.

Interrogative: the sentence asks a direct question.

Are you going to see that movie?

Imperative: the sentence expresses either a request or a demand.

Please don't be late.
Do the dishes now.

Exclamatory: the sentence indicates a strong feeling or emotion.

What a horrible accident that was!

Declarative and imperative sentences end with a period; an interrogative sentence ends with a question mark; and an exclamatory sentence ends with an exclamation mark.

A sentence that contains an indirect question is declarative in form and is therefore followed by a period, *not* by a question mark. An indirect question is usually introduced by the words *if* or *whether.*

Direct: Is he going to the office?

Indirect: I wonder whether he is going to the office.

A sentence that is declarative or imperative can also be made a question by using a question mark rather than the period.

Declarative: That is your answer.
That is your answer?
Imperative: Stay until it's over.
Stay until it's over?

Structure. In addition to classifying them according to purpose, sentences can be classified according to structure. This classification is based on identifying the number and kinds of subject-predicate ingredients found in the sentence.

According to grammatical structure, there are four kinds of sentences: simple, compound, complex, and compound-complex.

Simple sentence. A grammatically complete group of words with one subject and one predicate is a *simple sentence.* However, either the subject or the predicate, or both, may be compound.

Mary danced.

Mary and Jane danced.

Mary and Jane danced and sang.

Mary in her blue costume and Jane in her red costume danced in the park and sang standing on a bench.

Simple does not mean short, nor does it mean uncomplicated. It merely means that there is one basic subject-predicate unit.

Compound sentence. Two or more basically equal subject-predicate units joined together by *and, but, or, nor, for, yet,* or *so* make a *compound sentence.*

Sarah ate her whole lunch, and Margie ate only her orange.

These two or more simple sentences, called main or independent clauses in the compound sentence, may also be joined by a semicolon.

The rent was late, and they didn't have the money to pay it.

The rent was late; they didn't have the money to pay it.

Complex sentence. The combination of one main or independent clause with one dependent or subordinate clause is called a *complex sentence.* A subordinate clause is a group of words that contains a subject-predicate unit but cannot stand alone.

Although the subordinate clause has a subject and a predicate, it cannot function as a sentence; it must be joined with the independent clause by the use of subordinate conjunctions to make complete sense. See Unit 17 for a list of subordinate conjunctions needed to construct complex sentences.

Since she left the house late, she did not arrive at school on time.

Using a subordinate clause alone creates the common sentence fault called a sentence fragment (see p. 109).

He certainly matured. *After he went away to college.*

Compound-complex sentence. A *compound-complex sentence* contains two or more independent clauses and one or more subordinate clauses.

The children went to bed early, but they couldn't sleep because they were too tired.

PRACTICE. Identify the following sentences according to purpose by writing **D** for declarative, **INT** for interrogative, **IMP** for imperative, and **E** for exclamatory in the blanks at right.

1. How beautiful the baby is! _____

2. The baby is beautiful. _____

3. Get to bed this minute. _____

4. Were you ready to leave? _____

5. I wonder whether our nurse, Stephanie Hassani,

   is ready. _____

   Identify the following sentences according to structure by writing **S** for simple, **CD** for compound, **CX** for complex, and **CD-CX** for compound-complex in the blanks at right.

6. If the weather remains good, we'll take the boat trip

   around the harbor tomorrow. _____

7. Many American cities are extremely concerned about

   air pollution. _____

8. Storm patterns, sunspots, and radioactivity are detected and

   recorded by weather satellites. _____

9. When her father became ill, she determined to care for him

   herself so that he would not have to be confined to a nursing

   home. _____

10. Some people interested in the money market trade in short-

    term securities, and others trade in common stocks. _____

Clauses and sentences. The relation between the clause and the sentence is an essential one. The *independent clause* has a complete subject and a complete predicate, and it makes sense standing alone; therefore, it is also a sentence. The independent clause does not create the problems that the dependent clause creates in the sentence. Therefore, it is important to understand the *dependent clause* to avoid errors in the structure of the sentence. A dependent clause may be a part of an independent clause.

Although the storm was heavy, the taxi driver, *who had years of driving experience*, was able to navigate through the rain.

The dependent clause *who had years of driving experience* is part of the independent clause *the taxi driver was able to navigate through the rain.*

Many complex sentences contain dependent clauses introduced by the pronouns *that, which*, and *who*. These pronouns are called *relative pronouns* because they show the relation between the antecedent and the dependent clause.

The saleswoman who came to the office yesterday is here again today.

In the example above, the relative pronoun *who* shows the relation between the antecedent *saleswoman* and the dependent clause *who came into the office yesterday.*

Sentence fragment. It has been noted above that dependent or subordinate clauses written as though they were sentences create a sentence structure problem called the *fragment*. The sentence fragment is an isolation of the basic subject-verb unit and indicates incomplete or confused thinking. The fragment is just a piece of a thought, beginning with a capital, ending with a period, and pretending to be a sentence.

She went to Manor Hall College. Which is a beautiful school.

Here, the dependent clause *which is a beautiful school* cannot stand alone. It is a sentence fragment.

In addition to using dependent clauses as though they can stand alone, there are other ways to create sentence fragments. A phrase or any other word group that does not contain the independent subject-verb unit becomes a fragment when written to stand alone.

Many people detest Sundays. All that inactivity, all that time.

As is obvious from the example above, many sentence fragments can often be corrected by incorporating them with the preceding sentence.

Sentence fragments are sometimes accepted in creative writing for effect. Their usage, however, is incorrect for most practical purposes.

Fused sentence. The *fused sentence* occurs when two independent clauses are joined without the use of the coordinating conjunction or the semicolon.

Alice is an energetic girl she plays tennis twice a day.

This fault can be corrected by creating two separate sentences, by inserting a semicolon or a comma and a coordinating conjunction, or by inserting a subordinating conjunction.

Comma splice. The *comma splice*, or *comma fault*, occurs when a comma, rather than a coordinating conjunction or semicolon, is used between two independent clauses.

He goes to a ball game every week, sometimes he goes twice.

Except for a series of short clauses, the comma cannot be used to separate two independent clauses. This fault is easily corrected by replacing the comma with a semicolon or by inserting a conjunction.

Run-on sentence. Both the fused sentence and the comma splice are types of *run-on sentences*, but there is a more loosely defined run-on sentence that consists of excessive coordination or excessive subordination.

Excessive coordination is piling up independent clauses joined by *and, but, so*, etc.

The young teacher planned all her lessons and was able to work all her plans but she became so exhausted that she couldn't correct all the papers and she

started losing sleep and she lost a lot of weight so she finally decided to resign.

Excessive subordination is stringing together too many subordinate clauses in one sentence.

If Bill can make it to the dance when Joe comes home for the holidays, Bill hopes to use the new car which his father bought him because of his excellent grades that put him on the honor roll, unless Joe would rather ride in his own car.

PRACTICE. Underline the dependent clauses in the following sentences. If there is no dependent clause in the sentence, write **none** at the end of the sentence.

1. She was sure that her sister, who practiced every day, would win the race. _____

2. Coming to the city, New York, he was amazed at the traffic. _____

3. If all went well, the chairperson promised to recognize Harry and me. _____

4. Everyone in the neighborhood agreed to complain to the police about the robberies that were occurring with increasing frequency in the area. _____

5. Although the children went to bed, they were unable to sleep because of the heat. _____

> In the following sentences, identify the sentence fault by writing **F** for fragment, **CS** for comma splice, **FS** for fused sentence, and **R-ON** for other types of run-on sentences in the blanks at right. If there is no sentence fault, write **none**.

6. Magellan was a great navigator, he sailed around the world. _____

7. Being in a position of great authority. _____

8. She looked out across the lake it was so pretty and peaceful. _____

9. The witness was so frightened by the accused man that she was unwilling to testify she began to cry. _____

10. Although he always voted for civil rights legislation and was considered a liberal, he disliked being labeled that way and chastised reporters for using the term *liberal*, which he considered inaccurate, and he felt this constituted sloppy reporting. _____

UNIT 22 ▽ APPLICATION

Kinds of Sentences

Fill in the blanks with the participle formed from the verb printed in parentheses. Identify the kind of sentence by writing **D** for declarative, **INT** for interrogative, **IMP** for imperative, and **E** for exclamatory in the blanks at right.

For
Scoring

1. Were you really _____ the company by that

   action. (benefit)   _____ _____

2. Please spend your time _____. (study)   _____ _____

3. I asked if the package was still _____ on the

   table. (lie)   _____ _____

4. I hope that you are _____ yourself to your work

   all the time. (apply)   _____ _____

5. What a _____ experience that was. (disappoint)   _____ _____

6. Just what are the _____ facts in this

   case. (underlie)   _____ _____

7. We are _____ with your request. (comply)   _____ _____

8. How _____ the accident was. (depress)   _____ _____

9. Mr. Jackson is _____ with the president right

   now. (confer)   _____ _____

10. I wonder whether the company is _____ to that

    policy. (commit)   _____ _____

Identify the following sentences according to structure by writing **S** for simple, **CD** for compound, **CX** for complex, **CD-CX** for compound-complex, **C-S** for comma splice, and **F-S** for fused sentence in the blanks at right. If the word group is any other kind of run-on, write **R-ON**. If the word group is not a sentence, write **F** for fragment.

11. Although Sandra likes to sing, she does not enjoy hearing

    the opera.   _____ _____

12. I shall give you permission to go, but you must come in on time. _____ ____

13. Until spring comes, the winter days will be oppressive and I shall be bored. _____ ____

14. Being old and arrogant and never wanting to give in. _____ ____

15. Though he was above average in height, he would not admit to being tall. _____ ____

16. Reading the daily news did not appeal to him. _____ ____

17. She won. _____ ____

18. Squealing with laughter. _____ ____

19. She went to the store in the morning, she bought him a hat. _____ ____

20. When they went to the park, the ranger told them there were no more campsites, however, they went to a friend's yard to pitch their tent. _____ ____

21. People like to do portraits of themselves. _____ ____

22. Although many famous painters have captured striking likenesses of themselves, amateur photographers are often also successful at self-portraiture. _____ ____

23. To some photographers, the most interesting subject is the self. _____ ____

24. Individuality can be expressed more creatively in self-photography, and the difficult techniques and skills needed to take your own picture can be mastered by practice. _____ ____

25. There are endless possibilities for experimentation and discovery there are no limits to self-expression in photographic self-portraiture. _____ ____

UNITS 20–22 ▽ RECAP

Phrases ▽
Voice and Mood of Verbs ▽
Kinds of Sentences

Here are the highlights of the guides relating to phrases, the voice and mood of verbs, and kinds of sentences.

Phrases. A phrase is a group of closely related words that does not have a subject and a predicate. There are several kinds of phrases: noun phrase; verb phrase; verbal phrases (participial phrase, infinitive phrase, and gerund phrase); prepositional phrases (adjective phrase, adverb phrase, and noun phrase); appositive phrase; absolute phrase; and elliptical phrase.

Voice. The voice of the verb is the distinction which shows whether the subject acts or is acted upon, thereby making clear the relationship between the subject and the action of the verb. If the subject performs the action, the verb is in the active voice. If the subject receives the action, the verb is in the passive voice. Only transitive verbs have a passive voice.

Mood. The mood or mode of the verb designates the manner in which action, being, or state is expressed. There are three moods of the verb: indicative, imperative, and subjunctive.

Types of sentences. Sentences are classified according to purpose and according to structure. The four kinds of sentences according to purpose are: declarative, interrogative, imperative, and exclamatory. The four kinds of sentences according to structure are: simple, compound, complex, and compound-complex.

Fragments. Dependent or subordinate clauses written as though they were sentences are fragments. Subordinate clauses always function as nouns, adjectives, or adverbs and must relate to the main clause.

Other non-sentences. Common sentence faults are the fused sentence, the comma splice, and the run-on sentence, especially excessive coordination and excessive subordination.

In the sentences below, determine which illustrates the guide indicated. Write the correct letter in the blank at the right.

For Scoring

1. Noun phrase.
   a. The firemen *will have been shown* how to use the equipment.
   b. *The frequently vandalized old schoolhouse* will be torn down. _____ _____

2. Gerund phrase.
   a. *Miniature painting* was his hobby.
   b. *The miniature painting* won a prize. _____ _____

3. Participial phrase.
   a. The Honor Society *was having a reception*.
   b. *Having a reception*, the Honor Society sent out invitations. _____ _____

4. Infinitive phrase used as an adverb.
   a. He traveled *to broaden his experience*.
   b. He needed enough money *to travel*. _____ _____

5. Prepositional adjective phrase.
   a. The principal believed that the teacher *with the best discipline* was a better teacher.
   b. The teacher shouted *with impatient anger* to control the class. _____ _____

6. Appositive phrase.
   a. Wilson was the president *who wrote the famous fourteen points*.
   b. Woodrow Wilson, *the author of the famous fourteen points*, did an unwitting disservice to Poland. _____ _____

7. Passive voice of the verb.
   a. The carton was seen lying in the shipping room.
   b. I saw the carton lying in the shipping room. _____ _____

8. Imperative mood of the verb.
   a. She was asked to arrange the flowers.
   b. Please arrange the flowers. _____ _____

9. Subjunctive mood of the verb.
   a. Were it up to me, I would authorize the raises.
   b. I will authorize the raise when I become president. _____ _____

10. Declarative complex sentence.
    a. John is going to college because he wants to become a doctor.
    b. John is going to college, but he doesn't want to be a doctor. _____ _____

11. Subordinate clause as an adverb.
    a. He liked to sit on the porch when the summer nights were hot.
    b. He liked to sit on the porch, which was cool and comfortable. _____ _____

12. Sentence fragment.
    a. Good medical care in hospitals usually produces high costs.
    b. Usually producing high costs of good medical care. _____ _____

13. Comma fault or comma splice.
    a. She went to the store, they didn't have what she needed.
    b. She went to the store; they didn't have what she needed. _____ _____

14. Fused sentence.
    a. Fred is an athlete he wins all the races.
    b. Fred is an athlete who wins all the races. _____ _____

15. Run-on sentence.
    a. Although she wanted to visit Disney World with her children, she could not go because her daughter became ill.
    b. Although she wanted to visit Disney World with her children and she wanted to show them other parts of Florida, she could not go because her daughter became ill they will go another time. _____ _____

Underline the guide in parentheses that applies to each of these sentences.

16. Cynthia in her ballet costume and Alice in school uniform still looked and acted like twins. (Simple sentence, Compound sentence) _____

17. Be here at six o'clock. (Declarative sentence, Imperative sentence) _____

18. The company was planning to remodel all the offices by spring. (Active voice, Passive voice) _____

19. Eating desserts has made him fat. (Participial phrase, Gerund phrase) _____

20. The child cried with frustration. (Adjective phrase, Adverbial phrase) _____

UNIT 23
Common Words Often Misused

Sometimes words are confused because they are pronounced the same but have different spellings—such as *affect*, *effect*; *addition*, *edition*; *stationary*, *stationery*; and *accept*, *except*. The way to master them is to learn their meanings and memorize which spellings go with which meanings.

To, Too, Two. *Too* is always an adverb and means *also* or *more than* enough. *To* is a preposition. *Two* is simply the numeral 2 written in letters.

If you *two* women are going *to* Chicago, I shall go *too*.

Their, There. *Their* is a pronoun. *There* is an adverb meaning *at that place*, or it can be used as a pronoun to introduce a sentence or clause.

There is no question that those men did *their* very best to be *there* on time.

Passed, Past. *Passed* is the past tense and perfect tense form of the regular verb *pass*: *I pass, I passed, I have passed*. Past is used as an adjective or noun and refers to *time before the present*. *Past* is also used as a preposition and as an adverb to mean *beyond*.

He *passed* the test in the *past* month.

That is *past* history.

He ran *past* me.

Advise, Advice. *Advise* is always a verb. Notice that the *s* is pronounced like a *z*. *Advice* is always a noun. The *c* is pronounced like *s*. Both words carry the idea of *an opinion offered as worthy to be followed.*

Although his mother gave him good *advice*, his father may *advise* him differently.

Adopt, Adapt. Both of these words are verbs. *Adopt* means *to take without change. Adapt* means *to change so as to make suitable.* The noun derived from *adopt* is *adoption.* The noun derived from *adapt* is *adaptation.*

We shall *adopt* the plan.

I am sure the plan can be *adapted* to our use.

Capital, Capitol. *Capital* is a noun or an adjective. As an adjective, it means *relating to the head; chief; foremost.* As a noun, it refers to a *sum of money. Capital* also refers to the city which is the *seat of government. Capitol* is the building in which the government body meets.

A sentence begins with a *capital* letter.

We draw interest on the *capital*.

Washington is the *capital* of the United States. The Senate holds its sessions in the *Capitol*.

Affect, Effect. *Affect* is always a verb meaning *to influence* or *act upon. Effect* is used both as a noun and as a verb. As a verb, it means *to bring about* or *to accomplish.* As a noun, it means a *result* or a *consequence.*

It is difficult to know how parents will *affect* their child. Their *effect* depends on both heredity and environment.

Do you hope to *effect* a settlement of the dispute?

Do you hope to *affect* a settlement of the dispute?

Principle, Principal. *Principle* is always a noun meaning *a rule of action.* (Notice that *principle* and *rule* both end in *le.*) *Principal* is generally used as an adjective meaning *first,* or *most important.* Sometimes, *principal* is used as a noun to mean *the first* or *most important* one. As a noun, it also means a *sum of money* at interest and the *head of a school.*

There is a basic *principle* that motivates our behavior.

What is your *principal* objection to the plan?

Who is the *principal* of your school?

Don't draw on the *principal* you have saved.

Accept, Except. *Accept* is always a verb meaning *to take* or *receive. Except* is usually a preposition that means *leaving out* or *but.* Sometimes, *except* is used as a verb meaning *to leave out.*

We are happy to *accept* your invitation.

There is no one here *except* me.

I hope you will *except* me from the list of candidates.

Counsel, Council. *Counsel* is used as both a noun and a verb. As a noun, it means *advice* or the *one who gives advice*, such as a lawyer. As a verb, *counsel* means *to advise* or to *give advice*. *Council* is always a noun meaning *a body of people* who come together for deliberation.

What counsel can you give on this matter?

Mr. Sawyer is my *counsel* in this case.

The city *council* meets tonight.

Formally, Formerly. Both these words are always *adverbs*. *Formally* means *in a way established by custom*. *Formerly* simply means *before*.

Don't wait until you are *formally* introduced. That was the custom *formerly*.

Canvas, Canvass. *Canvas* is always a noun meaning a *heavy coarse cloth*. *Canvass* is used both as a noun and as a verb. It carries the idea of *investigating* or *investigation* and also *soliciting* orders.

The sails were made of quality *canvas*.

Did you *canvass* all the offices?

Each election is preceded by a *canvass* of the voters.

PRACTICE. Choose the correct form of the words in parentheses and write them in the blanks.

1. (to, too, two)   The children were _____ excited _____ sit still.

2. (principle, principal)   The _____ of the school said the students must act on _____ .

3. (counsel, council)   The church _____ members voted to engage legal _____ .

4. (advise, advice)   When you ask someone for _____ , be sure he is able to _____ you well.

5. (affect, effect)   We are never sure how we _____ others or what the _____ of our words may be when we speak critically or controversially.

6. (formerly, formally)   _____ , it was customary to respond in writing, but now people don't do things so _____ .

7. (canvas, canvass)   They made a _____ of all the sporting goods stores to find the quality _____ they needed.

8. (their, there)   _____ sails were bought over _____ in the boat supply shop.

9. (capital, Capitol)   Washington, our _____ , is identified with pictures of the _____ building.

Precede, Proceed. Both of these words are always verbs. *Precede* means *to go* or *come before*. *Proceed* means *to move forward* or *to carry on*. Notice that the noun derived from *proceed* is spelled *procedure*.

What words did we list to *precede* these?

I wish you would *proceed* with the work.

What is the correct *procedure*?

Stationery, Stationary. *Stationery* is generally used as a noun but may also be used as an adjective to modify a noun (the *stationery* store). It refers to *articles used in writing*—paper, envelopes, etc. *Stationary* is an adjective meaning *standing still, not moving about*. Associating the *e* in *stationery* with the *e* in *envelope* may help you remember the difference.

Our office *stationery* bills are high.

The laundry room has *stationary* tubs.

Leased, Least. *Leased* is the past tense and perfect form of the regular verb *lease*, meaning *to rent*. *Least* is the superlative of *little*. It is used as a noun, an adjective, and an adverb.

Our company *leased* cars from the *least* expensive dealer.

Respectfully, Respectively. Both of these words are adverbs. *Respectfully* means *in a polite way, with respect*. *Respectively* means *in that order*.

We *respectfully* refer you to our records.

These matters are fully discussed on pages 5, 8, 9, and 14, *respectively*.

Weather, Whether. *Weather* is used as a noun meaning the *state of the climate*. Sometimes it is used as a verb to mean *to come through safely*. *Whether* is a conjunction used to introduce a clause that indicates a choice.

We have had fine *weather*.

The ship will *weather* the storm.

I do not know *whether* we shall go.

Coarse, Course. *Coarse* is always an adjective meaning *rough* or *rude*. *Course* is generally used as a noun meaning a *line of action* or *conduct*. *Of course* is an expression meaning *certainly*. *Course* can also refer to a *route* or to a *subject of study*.

That paper is too *coarse* for our needs.

He was thought of as a *coarse* person.

What *course* shall we follow?

I am taking a *course* in marine biology.

Compliment, Complement. These words are used both as nouns and as verbs. *Compliment* means an *expression of praise*. *Complement* is *that which completes*. Notice the adjectives derived from these nouns: *complimentary, complementary*. As an aid in remembering the difference, notice that the first six letters of *complement* and *complete* are the same.

That was a nice *compliment* you paid her.

That was a *complimentary* remark.

The regiment has its full *complement* of men.

A *complementary* shipment helped to fill the order.

Sight, Site, Cite. *Sight* is generally a noun meaning *view*. It can sometimes be used as a verb, such as *to sight the enemy*. *Site* is always a noun meaning *location*. *Cite* is always a verb meaning *to refer to, to give an example, to commend, to summon* (as in citation to court), or *to reprimand officially and demand correction*.

They were in *sight* of the mountains.

It was a good *site* for camping.

Can you *cite* the examples for the rule?

The health department may *cite* you for those violations.

Eminent, Imminent. These words are adjectives. *Eminent* means *high in merit, distinguished*. *Imminent* means *close at hand* and implies danger.

The speaker is an *eminent* professor.

A storm seems *imminent*.

Access, Excess. Both of these words are nouns. *Access* means *permission or ability to enter or approach*. *Excess* means *more than the required amount*. The adjectives formed from these nouns are *accessible* and *excessive*.

Poland must have *access* to the sea.

This requirement is not in *excess* of European commitments.

Conscience, Conscious. *Conscious* is an adjective that means *aware* or *not asleep*. *Conscience* is a noun meaning the ability to *recognize right and wrong*.

Conrad was *conscious* of the psychological complexity of their relationship. His *conscience* would not permit him to misuse their friendship.

PRACTICE. Choose the correct form of the words in parentheses and write them in the blanks.

---

1. (sight, site, cite)   Within _____ of the lake, they found they could _____ many reasons for selecting this _____ for camp.

2. (proceed, precede)   Those who _____ us sometimes show us how to _____ .

3. (respectfully, respectively)   Since they did not behave _____ , Gus, Tony, and Philip, _____ , were ordered to bed.

4. (compliment, complement)   Because he had a full _____ of excellent men, the general received a _____ in the president's speech.

5. (coarse, course)   He always wore a _____ jacket on the rough riding _____ .

6. (weather, whether)   In this warm _____ , I don't know _____ to order more oil.

7. (stationary, stationery)   She used fine _____ to order new _____ tubs from the catalog.

8. (eminent, imminent)   Some of the country's _____ statesmen believed that war was _____ .

9. (leased, least)   Sometimes these apartments are _____ by people who seem _____ likely to be good tenants.

10. (access, excess)   Those who drink to _____ often find they don't have _____ to family parties.

11. (conscious, conscience)   Dostoevski believed that as we become more _____ , we develop a higher _____ .

12. (weather, whether)   We shall have to go to Chicago _____ the _____ is good or bad.

13. (course, coarse)   While taking his _____ , he was disgusted at everyone's _____ manners.

UNIT 23 ▽ APPLICATION

Common Words Often Misused

Choose the correct form of the words in parentheses and write them in the blanks.

For
Scoring

1. _____ for two points, we _____ all your proposals. (accept, except) ____

2. There were _____ many applicants for the few vacancies at that school. (to, too, two) ____

3. She didn't know _____ she wanted to join a sorority. (weather, whether) ____

4. The teacher said the assignments dealt with pages 4, 9, 12, and 15, _____ . (respectfully, respectively) ____

5. They tried to manage their money by not touching the _____ . (principle, principal) ____

6. Mr. Ames was uncertain of how to _____ to the next step. (precede, proceed) ____

7. The people on the Gulf Coast of Florida were warned that the hurricane was _____ . (imminent, eminent) ____

8. He could not _____ the provisions of the Preamble to the Constitution. (sight, site, cite) ____

9. It is difficult for most people to _____ charity. (except, accept) ____

10. Those who refuse to _____ to change remain outside the mainstream. (adapt, adopt) ____

11. The architects cited the new state _____ for its unusual design. (capital, capitol) ____

12. For centuries _____ , the Eskimos have managed to survive in the cold. (past, passed) ____

13. Psychologists tell us we must have _____ to our hidden feelings. (excess, access)   ____

14. He had his coat of arms printed on his _____ . (stationary, stationery)   ____

15. The Indians designed jewelry that showed pride in _____ heritage. (there, their)   ____

16. She was _____ known as Miss Jones, but now she prefers to be addressed as Ms. (formerly, formally)   ____

17. He wondered what _____ he would have on the vote. (affect, effect)   ____

18. The Santa Balboa City _____ was criticized for passing the amendment. (Counsel, Council)   ____

19. Sometimes the most famous are the _____ deserving of hero status. (leased, least)   ____

20. The politician planned to _____ the neighborhood to see how the people felt about the issue. (canvas, canvass)   ____

21. The teacher warned that the belligerent student's _____ of action would get her expelled. (coarse, course)   ____

22. The student did not accept the teacher's _____ about apologizing. (advice, advise)   ____

23. There are many ways to _____ a person without being dishonest. (complement, compliment)   ____

24. Because of her _____ , the social worker cared about the needs of the poor. (conscious, conscience)   ____

25. One of the aims of education is to make us more _____ of our responsibilities to society at large. (conscious, conscience)   ____

UNITS 1–23 ▽ OVERVIEW

Select the correct word from the parentheses and write it in the space provided at the right.

For
Scoring

1. The study of (english, English) is a lifelong pursuit. _____ _____

2. He is sad that the daily news (is, are) depressing. _____ _____

3. The faculty met to approve all the (curriculi, curricula). _____ _____

4. She (don't, doesn't) know when the new team begins. _____ _____

5. A new supply of paper and envelopes (is, are) needed. _____ _____

6. Many (attorneys, attornies) in the Phoenix area graduated

   from local law schools. _____ _____

7. Only one of the foreign cars (was, were) sold at auction. _____ _____

8. There were no Ls, but several size (9's, 9s) remained. _____ _____

9. A student is rated by the quality of (her, their) tests. _____ _____

10. Everyone in the club (is, are) doing volunteer work. _____ _____

11. Nobody but Ann and (I, me) came to the meeting. _____ _____

12. Each of the musicians (was, were) complimented. _____ _____

13. The jury (has, have) argued among themselves for hours. _____ _____

14. Either Mr. Martinez or his assistants (is, are) to be

    credited with the victory. _____ _____

15. Many children (have swam, have swum) safely because

    of Red Cross instruction. _____ _____

16. Every one of them agrees that (his or her, their) property

    is important. _____ _____

17. We accept the responsibility for taking care of what is

    (our's, ours). _____ _____

18. How will this ruling (affect, effect) us? _____ _____

19. A set of specifications (is, are) being prepared. _____ _____

20. The photograph was taken on the (Capitol, Capital) steps. _____ _____

21. (Who, Whom) should I see when I stop by? _____ _____

22. She still believes in (Moses's, Moses') laws. _____ _____

23. I suggested that he (lay, lie) down for an hour. _____ _____

24. (Children's, Childrens') coats are sold upstairs. _____ _____

25. We have no more of (this, these) kind left. _____ _____

26. The new officers were (formerly, formally) presented. _____ _____

27. Our business has increased (considerable, considerably). _____ _____

28. If you were (I, me), what would you do? _____ _____

29. The fruit certainly tastes (sweetly, sweet). _____ _____

30. She is one of the employees who (is, are) always on time. _____ _____

31. A number of applicants (is, are) to be interviewed. _____ _____

32. We (shall, will) look forward to hearing from you. _____ _____

33. Mr. Strong, (who, whom) I met recently, will call on you. _____ _____

34. Do you want any of (we, us) representatives to come? _____ _____

35. Between you and (I, me), I doubt that statement. _____ _____

36. Everybody wanted to voice (his or her, their) opinion. _____ _____

37. He deserves a two (week's, weeks') vacation. _____ _____

38. We have no use for (those, that) kind of machine. _____ _____

39. Miss Ping can do the work as well as (I, me). _____ _____

40. The pipe is (broke, broken) in two places. _____ _____

41. It was (she, her) who made the pottery. _____ _____

42. In the afternoon she (laid, lay) down for an hour. _____ _____

43. The plan is different (from, than) the one submitted by
    last year's committee. _____ _____

44. I'm sure that I (was been seen, was seen) at the hall. _____ _____

45. I (will have been, shall have been) present at all the
    Mozart concerts this summer. _____ _____

46. After testing my sister and (I, me), the director accepted
    us in the chorus. _____ _____

47. She was worried about the danger of (his, him) failing the
    course. _____ _____

48. The work (did, done) by the children was magnificent. _____ _____

49. Could it have been (them, they) who sent the flowers? _____ _____

50. I shall appreciate (you, your) using this book. _____ _____

Answers to PRACTICE

UNIT 1

1. Many high performance (microphones) were sold. P
2. The (companies) with reliable annual reports succeed. P
3. The (takeover) of the small firm by the corporation is disappointing. S
4. A typewritten (set) of specifications for the job is enclosed. S
5. Graphic (designs) of good quality communicate. P
6. The effective company (president) deliberates. S
7. The (mimes, drummers) and (baton twirlers) are marching. P
8. Several differing (opinions) about the completion of the highway were voiced. P
9. The habitual (runner-up) tries. S
10. The camera (shops) in the shopping district were closed. P

---

1. (Each) of our salespeople sends in a daily report.
2. Most of the (credit) for the successful promotion goes to Mr. Sawyer.
3. The exact (meaning) of these legal words and phrases is given on page 289.
4. Large (amounts) of clothing are donated to the organization every month.
5. Elite Computer's wonderful word processing (systems) are on display around the world.
6. The fast-food (restaurant) served delicious fried chicken.
7. The magazine's (subscriptions) increased last year.
8. The (ventures) of the investment firm were under scrutiny.
9. (Systems) for solar heating were incorporated into the architect's design.
10. The telephone (wires) were replaced by flexible plastic tubing that transmitted sound.
11. Last year's sharp price (increases) caused a jump in the earnings chart.
12. (He) advocated curbing profits to inject new vigor into the market.

UNIT 2

1. bonuses
2. matches
3. Spaniards
4. sphinxes
5. pizzas
6. trees

1. countries
2. wolves
3. pulleys
4. agencies
5. thieves
6. sopranos

7. Badlands
8. buses
9. crashes
10. waltzes
11. stresses

7. cliffs
8. chimneys
9. loaves

UNIT 3

1. series
2. postmen
3. proceeds
4. geese
5. sheep
6. saleswomen
7. teeth
8. mathematics
9. species
10. children

1. phenomena *or* phenomenons
2. nuclei
3. curricula
4. criteria
5. prospecti
6. vertebrae *or* vertebras
7. media

UNIT 4

1. Our products (P) are made of natural ingredients, and they are sure to please.
2. If the papers (P) arrive, they will be held here.
3. The proofs (P) were ready yesterday, but they cannot be mailed until tomorrow.
4. A stenographer (S) cannot hope to get anywhere unless she knows English grammar.
5. The members (P) have agreed that we should go ahead with the plans.
6. Did Henry (S) say why he called?
7. Sharon, (S) will you be able to explain the procedures to the new employee?
8. The typewriter (S) was discarded because it was irreparable.
9. The president (S) has promised that she will address the members of the board.

---

1. Miss Smith said that **she** would return the favor.
2. The operator carefully explained what **he/she** had done.
3. Let Mr. Howard sharpen the scissors so that **they** will cut better.
4. The members of the committee all agreed that **they/we** should supply the funds.

5. Everyone did just what **he/she** was told to do.
6. The <u>cattle</u> were then put up for sale, and **they** brought a good price.
7. You **were** still reading that book when I saw you three weeks ago.
8. I believe you **have** made a mistake in the estimate.
9. You **are** the very person for whom I have been looking.

UNIT 5

1. I
2. L
3. I
4. T
5. T
6. T

---

1. are complying; complied; were complying
2. are disappointing; disappointed; were disappointing
3. is assisting; assisted; was assisting
4. am committing; committed; was committing
5. am planning; planned; was planning

UNIT 6

1. He appointed; we shall appoint
2. You carried; they will carry
3. She remitted; they will remit
4. They referred; you will refer
5. You wished; we shall wish

6. shall
7. will
8. will
9. shall
10. will

---

1. She has omitted; I had omitted
2. He has stayed; they had stayed
3. It has applied; you had applied
4. She has replied; they had replied
5. They have referred; we had referred

6. doesn't
7. doesn't
8. don't
9. doesn't

UNIT 7

1. am not

---

2. didn't
3. doesn't
4. haven't done
5. didn't
6. don't
7. hasn't done
8. weren't

9. did
10. has done
11. does; is
12. has done
13. were

---

1. chose; shall choose; has chosen
2. won; will win; has won
3. spoke; shall speak; has spoken
4. wrote; shall write; has written
5. forgot; will forget; has forgotten
6. drew; will draw; has drawn

UNIT 8

1. fell; shall fall; has fallen
2. forgave; will forgive; have forgiven
3. ate; will eat; have eaten
4. kept; shall keep; have kept
5. left; will leave; has left
6. led; will lead; have led
7. lost; shall lose; has lost

---

1. hurt; will hurt; has hurt
2. shut; will shut; has shut
3. overpaid; will overpay; have overpaid
4. stood; shall stand; has stood
5. came; shall come; have come
6. burst; will burst; has burst
7. quit; shall quit; has quit
8. let; shall let; has let
9. struck; will strike; have struck
10. put; shall put; have put

UNIT 9

1. She lay; you will lie; it has lain
2. He laid; I shall lay; you have laid
3. It lay; she will lie; they have lain
4. We lay; it will lie; we have lain
5. You laid; they will lay; I have laid
6. He lay; we shall lie; he has lain
7. She rose; we shall rise; he has risen
8. He raised; I shall raise; it has raised
9. It lay; they will lie; she has lain
10. We rose; it will rise; she has risen

1. She sat; we shall sit; you have sat
2. We saw; I shall see; they have seen
3. He set; you will set; I have set
4. We went; I shall go; he has gone
5. She sat; they will sit; she has sat
6. You went; they will go; it has gone
7. I saw; they will see; she has seen
8. I saw; we shall see; they have seen
9. You set; I shall set; you have set
10. We saw; I shall see; you have seen
11. I set; you shall set; I have set
12. I went; she will go; you have gone

UNIT 10

1. has
2. is
3. has
4. seems
5. is
6. comes
7. contains
8. has
9. doesn't

1. are
2. is
3. is
4. were
5. meets
6. disagree
7. is
8. is
9. have
10. was
11. are
12. is

UNIT 11

1. APP
2. SV
3. PN
4. SV
5. APP

1. company's
2. Manufacturers *or* Manufacturers'
3. brother's
4. women's
5. barber's
6. months'

UNIT 12

1. PN
2. S
3. APP
4. PN
5. S

1. its
2. his/her
3. his/her
4. its
5. its
6. his/her
7. their
8. his/her
9. its
10. its

UNIT 13

1. she
2. I
3. me/I
4. I
5. me/I

1. me
2. him
3. he
4. her
5. him
6. myself
7. himself

UNIT 14

1. earlier; earliest
2. lower; lowest
3. finer; finest
4. prettier; prettiest

1. He is **more** studious than his brother.
2. The woman had to go a **farther** distance than her daughter to get to the store.
3. The student is sometimes **more intelligent.**
4. That was the **most beautiful** music I had ever heard.
5. Of all the streets in the city, this one is the **narrowest.**
6. His work as an electrician was the **most dangerous** job he ever had.

7. There are many people of **Mexican** heritage in the Southwest.
8. Of all his subjects, he was **least** interested in math.

UNIT 15

1. an
2. the
3. a
4. a
5. an
6. an
7. an
8. an; the
9. an; the

1.	This	6.	Those
2.	These	7.	Those
3.	This	8.	Those
4.	These	9.	That
5.	These	10.	Those

11. these
12. Those
13. this
14. that

UNIT 16

1. We shall be <u>very</u> glad to come to your party. (degree)
2. Your payment is <u>considerably</u> overdue. (degree).
3. He worked <u>most carefully</u> by himself. (manner)
4. She came <u>here</u> to rest and relax. (place)

1. Adj.
2. Adv.
3. Adv.
4. Adj.
5. Adj.

6. He looked forward to college partly <u>because he had never lived away from home.</u>
7. <u>Unless her grades improve quickly,</u> she will fail the course.
8. We try to learn something about the native people <u>wherever we travel.</u>
9. <u>Although mortgages are difficult to obtain,</u> we plan to buy a house.
10. We'll all go to Hawaii <u>if you can spare the time.</u>

UNIT 17

1. He worried so much <u>about</u> the future that he could not get <u>through</u> the day.
2. Although her mother said the cat was <u>on</u> the roof, Tab was <u>under</u> the porch.
3. <u>During</u> the summer, he liked to spend time <u>with</u> his friends.
4. The assistant <u>in</u> the office brought the mail <u>for</u> all the managers.

5. her; from
6. with; her
7. He and I; between

1. <u>Neither</u> thunder <u>nor</u> lightning could frighten her dog. **CC**
2. She tried to buy a dress, <u>but</u> they didn't have her size. **C**
3. <u>Although</u> it was cloudy, it did not rain. **S**
4. <u>Since</u> his logic was faulty, he failed lamentably. **S**
5. <u>Both</u> Richard <u>and</u> Henry won athletic scholarships. **CC**
6. Neither George **nor** Paul **is** here at present.
7. Both energy **and** resourcefulness **are** required for this task.
8. Al is not **so** handsome as **he.**
9. Elizabeth is better than **he** at nailing up the panels.

UNIT 18

1. admitting; admitted; having admitted
2. preceding; preceded; having preceded
3. underlying; underlain, having underlain
4. preferring; preferred; having preferred
5. disappointing; disappointed; having disappointed
6. happening; happened; having happened
7. accepting; accepted; having accepted
8. arranging; arranged; having arranged
9. noticing; noticed; having noticed
10. winning; won; having won
11. transferring; transferred; having transferred
12. vying; vied; having vied
13. destroying; destroyed; having destroyed
14. committing; committed; having committed

15. b
16. a
17. b
18. b
19. a

1. singing; S
2. being; S

3. hiking; O
4. rearing; S
5. knitting; S
6. walking; S
7. begging, stealing; O

8. to work; ADV
9. to swim; N
10. to sell; AJ
11. to begin; ADV
12. to laugh; N

UNIT 19

1. whom
2. who
3. whose
4. who
5. whom
6. who
7. whom
8. whose

9. who
10. that
11. whom
12. was
13. are
14. whom
15. are
16. is

---

1. ADJ
2. N
3. N
4. ADJ
5. ADJ

6. The man who won the contest is going to Bermuda. **RES**
7. The saleswoman called on the prestigious Excelsior Company which is located two blocks from our office. **NONRES**
8. Jobs that pay well are difficult to find. **RES**
9. The president is a person whom everyone respects. **RES**
10. The unnecessary paperwork was locked in old files which were dusty and neglected. **NONRES**

UNIT 20

1. *Counting sheep* helps Consuela Petrucco fall asleep. **Verbal, G, N**
2. Margaret Underwood's new classical record *was warped*. **Verb phrase**
3. By the time he gets home, he *will have walked* three miles. **Verb phrase**

4. *Taking a deep breath*, Sue dived into the freezing water. **Verbal, P, Adj.**
5. They all stopped *to listen*. **Verbal, I, Adv.**
6. She has a strong ambition *to win the beauty contest*. **Verbal, I, Adj.**
7. *The little, old church on the hill* is attended by Richie Sargeant. **Noun phrase**
8. They *have been swimming* all morning. **Verb phrase**
9. *Vacationing in the Cayman Islands*, she overcame her grief. **Verbal, P, Adj.**
10. *Vacationing in the West Indies* is Matthew Martinovic's idea of luxury. **Verbal, G, N**

---

1. APP.
2. P. ADV.
3. P. ADJ.
4. P. NOUN
5. APP.
6. ELLIP.
7. ABSOL.
8. P. NOUN
9. P. ADV.
10. P. ADJ.
11. ABSOL.

UNIT 21

1. was given; has been given
2. was eaten; has been eaten
3. was done; has been done
4. was bought; has been bought
5. was begun; has been begun

6. The answer was given to Fernando by Martin.
7. The rudder was handled by Gerry De Freitas.
8. The lamp has been lit by Bobby Carpenter.
9. Two men were arrested by the officers.
10. New mortgages are no longer taken by the bank.

---

1. I
2. IMP
3. PF
4. S
5. IMP
6. PF
7. I
8. PF
9. IMP
10. PF
11. I
12. I
13. PF

UNIT 22

1. E

2. D
3. IMP
4. INT
5. D

6. CX
7. S
8. S
9. CD-CX
10. CD

1. She was sure that her sister, who practiced every day, would win the race.
2. none
3. If all went well, the chairperson promised to recognize Harry and me.
4. Everyone in the neighborhood agreed to complain to the police about the robberies that were occurring with increasing frequency in the area.
5. Although the children went to bed, they were unable to sleep because of the heat.

6. CS
7. F
8. FS
9. FS
10. R-ON

UNIT 23

1. The children were **too** excited **to** sit still.
2. The **principal** of the school said the students must act on **principle.**
3. The church **council** members voted to engage legal **counsel.**
4. When you ask someone for **advice**, be sure he is able to **advise** you well.
5. We are never sure how we **affect** others or what the **effect** of our words may be when we speak critically or controversially.
6. **Formerly,** it was customary to respond in writing, but now people don't do things so **formally.**
7. They made a **canvass** of all the sporting goods stores to find the quality **canvas** they needed.
8. **Their** sails were bought over **there** in the boat supply shop.
9. Washington, our **capital**, is identified with pictures of the **Capitol** building.

1. Within **sight** of the lake, they found they could **cite** many reasons for selecting this **site** for camp.
2. Those who **precede** us sometimes show us how to **proceed.**
3. Since they did not behave **respectfully**, Gus, Tony, and Philip, **respectively**, were ordered to bed.

4. Because he had a full **complement** of excellent men, the general received a **compliment** in the president's speech.
5. He always wore a **coarse** jacket on the rough riding **course.**
6. In this warm **weather**, I don't know **whether** to order more oil.
7. She used fine **stationery** to order new **stationary** tubs from the catalog.
8. Some of the country's **eminent** statesmen believed that war was **imminent.**
9. Sometimes these apartments are **leased** by people who seem **least** likely to be good tenants.
10. Those who drink to **excess** often find they don't have **access** to family parties.
11. Dostoevski believed that as we become more **conscious**, we develop a higher **conscience.**
12. We shall have to go to Chicago **whether** the **weather** is good or bad.
13. While taking his **course**, he was disgusted at everyone's **coarse** manners.